THE GOLDEN SUMMER

THE EDWARDIAN PHOTOGRAPHS
OF HORACE W. NICHOLLS

GAIL BUCKLAND

PAVILION
MICHAEL JOSEPH

CHAMPAGNE

Veuve Clicquot Ponsardin

MAISON FONDÉE EN 1772

REIMS
FRANCE

If the long summer days of King Edward's reign seem bathed in a golden light, it is surely the pale, sparkling gold of champagne. Of all champagnes, Veuve Clicquot was our Edwardian forefathers' first choice for every great event of the English Season.

Their cheerful call for "Another bottle of The Widow" still echoes down the years. Today, at Henley and Royal Ascot, at Goodwood and at Cowes, Veuve Clicquot remains 'the Champagne of the Season'.

With the Golden Summers of yesterday and tomorrow in mind, Veuve Clicquot Champagne is delighted to be associated with this tribute to a remarkable photographer.

CONTENTS

King Edward and Queen Alexandra riding
down the track on Gold Cup Day.
Royal Ascot, c. 1907

Edwardian high society added a little chapter – and surely the most recent, unless we are going to be silly about the 1920s – to the myth of the Lost Golden Age. During the years between the turn of the century and the First World War the glitter of rank, wealth and fashion was not confined to England . . . [it existed] with a considerable amount of cross-fertilization, assisted by a world press that employed more and more gossip-writers and photographers. But it was the English Edwardians who occupied and decorated the central position and did most to bring the myth of the Lost Golden Age into the twentieth century.

J. B. Priestley
The Edwardians, 1970

In those halcyon days, Cowes Regatta was the culminating function of the Season, and when it was over the Court retired to Balmoral. The aristocracy of England, who had, in theory, enjoyed one another's company since the previous May, went off to their grouse moors in Scotland and to their country estates . . . the last exhausted hostess relaxed her eighteen inch waist from the tortures of whalebone and steel. The debutantes tied the little bundles of dance programmes, with white pencils attached, placing them sentimentally in the handkerchief sachet, and wrote in their diaries: 'Another wonderfully exciting season has ended.' The last tired lady's maid pressed out the last ball-dress from Mr. Worth or Mr. Paquin, before dispatching it to some poor relation in the country. . . . The social top that had started spinning with the Court Presentations, gaining momentum with Ascot, Henley, Lord's and Goodwood, came to a standstill as the last rocket spent itself in the indigo sky of an August night at Cowes, which was the signal that the regatta was over.

Anthony Heckstall-Smith
Sacred Cowes, 1955

THE SUMMER NEVER TRULY ended for the privileged Edwardians until their world came to a complete and final halt in that fateful August of 1914. The party started, or so we nostalgically believe, with the death of Queen Victoria and the emergence of Edward VII, whose lifestyle differed so greatly from that of his austere parents. Gambling; chic clothes; shooting; sailing; pleasure trips to Paris, Continental watering–holes and spas; house parties and romantic entanglements and, of course, horse-racing became fashionable because Edward enjoyed them. He had trained from birth to be a ruler, and, as Queen

Victoria did not make him privy to the workings of government, his role became that of leader of Society.

It was not tantalizing to know what an old lady in perpetual mourning, even if she were a Queen and Empress, did all day. But a prince and king who dressed to the nines, who was a bit naughty and hedonistic, was something else. There was more gaiety and curiosity in the air than during Victoria's long reign.

Edwardians seemed to delight in public display, and this afforded photographers splendid opportunities to catch high and low society off-guard, dressed-up and having a good time. The beginning of the reign of King Edward VII saw the emergence of the photographically illustrated popular press. There had been ample wood-engravings in the second half of the nineteenth century, but photographs directly printed as halftone reproductions in one's own daily or weekly paper were so much more immediate, intimate and modern than anything that had been seen before.

The century was new and Edward was a new kind of king. The *Daily Mirror* in England, the first newspaper to be illustrated exclusively with photographs, appeared in January 1904. Horace Walter Nicholls (1867–1941), one of the world's best first-generation photojournalists, started recording Edwardian society at Henley that year and faithfully followed each seasonal event until the outbreak of war. His pictures of the Derby, Royal Ascot, Henley Regatta, Lord's, Goodwood, Cowes Regatta, grouse shooting, salmon fishing and the promenades, casinos, golf courses, and tennis courts on the French Riviera provide a unique glimpse into the national passions and preoccupations of the Edwardians. An enormously talented observer of expressions, fashions and human interactions at every level on the social scale, Nicholls was the premier British photographer of the period in this genre.

Nicholls made his reputation as a photojournalist during the Boer War. Now, at the beginning of the century, he turned his camera on sporting events to explore British national character and conventions. 'The Season', most of which involved competition of one sort or another, is the focus of his most memorable Edwardian photographs. With each glass plate exposed he highlighted how the British can be so strongly bound together and simultaneously so stratified. A contemporary newspaper analysing Edward VII's popularity wrote: '. . . to a large circle still he is a typical Englishman, and that is a character which cannot be fully attained except by one who shows himself to be in sympathy with that love of sport which is almost a passion with all ranks and classes in this country.'[1] The German Chancellor Bismarck wrote after one of Edward VII's Derby wins: 'You will never have a revolution in England as long as you keep up your racing.'[2] And C. B. Fry, a cricketer and Edwardian renaissance man wrote: 'A modern democracy without racing and cricket in the summer and football in the winter is, of course, unimaginable.'[3]

The aristocracy and the populace all went to the races and placed bets. If one's horse was in the lead, hearts pumping blue blood went as fast as those pumping the more ordinary kind. '. . . the humblest devotees of horse racing in a Derby day crowd,' wrote Keith Middlemas in *The Life and Times of Edward VII*, 'knew that King Edward was there to enjoy the national festival in precisely the same spirit as themselves. . . . There was, in fact, a real sympathy and community of feeling between himself and his people.' Royalty and those entitled to be *near* royalty had the advantage of the finish line being directly in front of their cordoned area, but the crowds at the Derby, rich and poor, were there for the excitement and the fun of it.

When, in 1896, the Prince of Wales won the Derby with Persimmon, 'the Downs echoed from one end to another with the cheers that were renewed again and again. Even the most dignified individuals in the stands for once let themselves go, and it was a truly remarkable exhibition of spontaneous enthusiasm and delight.'[4] That there could be one voice, outside of wartime, in a crowd so economically and socially diverse, attests not only to the prestige of monarchy, but to the national love of sport and, inherent in that, the belief that the best – man, woman or horse – wins in the end.

'Racing provided the answers to most of the Edwardians' loves and priorities: the ability to spend money and gamble, beautiful horses and fashionable women, excitement and gossip, the excuse for a house party, and most important, royal patronage,'[5] asserted George Plumptre, an expert on the subject of Edwardian horse-racing. If 'house party' is changed to 'party' and 'fashionable women' to 'women', we have an analysis that crosses class boundaries, albeit a sexist one.

Nicholls loved being there, among the crowds, isolating significant details and observing emotional and physical juxtapositions. A less able, or less confident, photographer could never get the telling pictures that Nicholls so frequently brought back from his excursions. Only in his youth was he a portrait photographer working in a studio: first as an apprentice to his father; again as an apprentice to a chemist in Huddersfield; during his adventurous years in Chile in the 1880s; while at the Cartland studio in Windsor, and when he first went to Johannesburg in the 1890s. After his success as a war correspondent during the Boer War, he decided upon his return to Britain in 1902 to attempt to enter the risky business of freelance photojournalism which, at that time, was just becoming a profession. Joining one of the newly formed picture agencies would have offered Nicholls more security, but he wanted to be able to choose and create his own stories and follow his own instincts.

Individuals pursuing communal pleasures kindled Nicholls' imagination. As early as the late 1890s his hobby had been to photograph the crowds at horse-racing events and polo meets in South Africa while earning his living taking the portraits of Boers and Uitlanders. In both his early and later work he came in close to see the faces in the crowds and stood back to see the flow patterns made by richly clothed or modestly attired bodies. His pictures affirm that humans, as a race, crave and enjoy company.

During the Edwardian period, Horace Nicholls made his living selling photographs to the press. Then, as now, the best market was for pictures of celebrities. Nicholls, however, was too democratic to specialize in just the more profitable end of the economic spectrum and turned his lens on all types of people. There is a picture at the Derby (page 38) showing the Vanderbilt lunch table laid with a linen cloth and folded serviettes, rosebuds in vases, wine and liqueur glasses, mustard pots, a cruet set, china plates and demi-tasse coffee cups. There is a manservant to serve the picnic, all of which takes place under a scalloped canopy in the coach and car park. The scene is passive, hands are all hidden, and the five seated at the table need exert no more energy than to raise fork to mouth, glass to lips. A head turned in conversation, a hand reaching into a pocket, perhaps to get a match to light the cigar already on the table, are the only observable motions.

Another view of efforts to satisfy hunger at the Derby (page 39) shows men scrambling at the gates, holding out bags and newspapers for scraps, a confusing scene of animated, needy people. Outstretched arms punctuate the picture, provide the emotional element; almost all the men are faceless. Nicholls titled this picture 'After the Derby (A Rush for Crumbs which Fall from the Rich Man's Table)'. The accoutrements on the rich man's table contrast poignantly with the folded newspapers and the mesh bags that the poor men will use to carry whatever discarded food they are given.

Nicholls' mission was not to change society but to describe it. He showed the ways of the rich and the methods of the poor not to make a particular social statement, but because, like the proverbial mountain, they were there. Although working in a visual medium, he was also a story-teller and he sought diversity and contrast to make his tales richer.

As a freelancer, Nicholls never went to an event with a script and only sometimes with an assignment. He constantly looked not only for subjects that would make exciting pictures, but also for story ideas to develop. He captioned his photographs imaginatively and presented them in groups that provided provocative or informative juxtapositions. He advised art directors on the scores of publications he visited exactly how they should use his pictures, and even did his own layouts occasionally. If Nicholls photographed something atypical at a particular event, then he always provided a handle by which the editors could grab his image and use it successfully on the printed page. Frequently, he succeeded in getting a full page in a journal with a handsome by-line because he was not illustrating someone else's more familiar story, he was generating his own. Week after week one strong image, either a straight photograph or a photomontage, would be reproduced full-page and words like 'A Study by Horace W. Nicholls' would appear, asserting that this picture was on par with the more familiar engravings and lithographs that appeared elsewhere in the magazine and deserved the same kind of scrutiny reserved for looking at art.

Many photographers working in Britain in more recent years, Tony Ray-Jones, Homer Sykes, Patrick Ward and Martin Parr, for example, have followed in Nicholls' footsteps, probably without even knowing that they did so, and adopted the theme of 'a day off'. Nicholls, however, had singular stylistic habits for a photojournalist. He was strictly a press photographer working for newspapers and weekly journals, but he made both documentary and composite images.

To report on the event was never Nicholls' primary objective; to *express* what he witnessed was his goal. One of Nicholls' finest achievements was his ability to convey the intensity of his experiences at these seasonal events – the voluptuousness of the sails on the yachts at Cowes Regatta, the exhilaration at the fairground on the Downs at Epsom, the physicality of the crowd, the bliss of lying back in a punt on a warm summer's day and being consoled by the rocking of the river.

Nicholls defies what we assume was the role of the early photojournalists. Facts had their place for Nicholls, but not at the expense of a strong, graphic image. A photograph should explode with life if it is to have a life of its own. If, through cutting and pasting pictures together, he could better recreate what he felt at the time, or make a more memorable image, then he did it. He wrote:

> I had tried many times to depict the scene as I saw it [Derby Day crowds] from one point, but never seemed able to satisfy myself with one negative, and so, feeling that if I was a painter I could take the licence of introducing into my picture what I could see to the right or the left, I resolved to take similar licence with my photographs of the day as I saw it. . . .[6]

A strange aesthetic for a reporter, but photographic 'truth' for Nicholls was as much an emotional state as an actual one. Art photographers in the nineteenth century had combined negatives to make more pictorially resolved images and overcome technical limitations. But a photojournalist at the beginning of the twentieth century? The remarkably refreshing quality of Nicholls' work is that, as a body, it defies categorization. As the divisions within photography were being established – art photography, reportage, commercial, personal, amateur – Nicholls was knocking them down with vengeance. For him there was no photographic liturgy that could not, at times, be amended. Yet he knew that, whenever possible, a straight photograph keenly seen was the most powerful communicator of all.

The Golden Summer, then, is a look at two complementary subjects: the Edwardian Season and the photography of Horace W. Nicholls. It is difficult to understand his work without an appreciation of some of the idiosyncracies and priorities of the period, and it is an impoverished look at the Edwardians which does not include Nicholls' glorious pictures.

'The Edwardian was never a golden age,' J. B. Priestley coaxes us to remember, 'but seen across the dark years afterwards it could easily be mistaken for one.' It did, most assuredly have a golden glow, an optimistic, sunlit face that Nicholls brilliantly portrayed. Summer, as metaphor and as an actual description, however, was accurate. A perpetual summer was achieved by the upper classes. *The Graphic* of 8 June 1907 explains how:

> There are the London season, from the middle of May to August; the German–Bath season, from August to the middle of September; the country house season, from the middle of September to the middle of December; and the South of France season, from the middle of December to the middle of May. . . . The growth of cosmopolitanism throughout the world is an important and interesting feature of the time. . . . We are all exchanging our rich.

Although this is from a contemporary source, the actual timing might have been slightly different, and certainly Scotland was the destination of many, including the royal family, after the 'last rocket spent itself in the indigo sky of an August night at Cowes'. But the implication is clear: the rich left for the Riviera rather than spend too many grey, cold days at home. It was this retreat to the South of France that gave the golden summer its never-ending quality.

Nicholls depicts the relocation to the Continent as the time, as on a hot summer's afternoon, when one falls asleep and starts to dream. A mask is put on, a stranger's hand is clasped, and one dances anonymously on the street – or so it seems in Nicholls' sensual depiction of these alien activities that drew the British to the Nice Carnival (pages 106–11). The glue that holds society so rigidly in the moderate British climate seems, at times, to get diluted, weakened in the damp heat of the Riviera sun. The grotesque quality of the Nice Carnival, the costumes, floats, bosoms and buttocks, is seductive and repulsive. It all seems the antithesis of the famous sense of good taste of the English upper class. There is a King and Queen of the Carnival, but they are huge caricatures made of papier mâché and a perversion of the words as the aristocracy of Britain understood them. How much the British participated in these flights of fantasy and emotional release, and how much they were voyeurs, it is difficult to determine. We only know for certain that Nicholls repeatedly went to the South of France because the British public craved to see, in the quiet of their homes, another alternative, civilized culture at play. And he found a market for these pictures in French publications as well.

Monte Carlo meant gambling but also more typical British pursuits – golf, tennis, croquet by day; dancing, music, cards at night. As it was common to say, sooner or later all the world (of British society) could be seen in the gambling rooms. Again the clothes were glorious, competition was strong, money could be made or lost, risk replaced security. Nicholls recognized his subject and photographed it faithfully. Perhaps because of light casting strong shadows and creating sharp outlines, many of his pictures from the South of France have a stark, frozen quality – a fly in amber, a remembrance of things past.

Of all the 'seasons' outlined in *The Graphic*, only the German–Bath one does not appear among Nicholls' existing negatives. An absolutely devoted family man, his own family albums attest that he was probably playing on the beach with his children and nieces and nephews when the court went to their spas to take off the extra weight gained in the preceding three months.

Nicholls' own life was in direct contrast to those he frequently portrayed at both ends of the economic ladder. He was middle-class, with decidedly artistic tendencies. Two girls at Sandown, Isle of Wight, Nicholls' favourite seaside resort (he lived there as a boy), look as if they could be members of Nicholls' family (page 103) – they have the Nicholls spirit, that sense of play that one sees over and over again in the family albums. Nicholls may have been able to market this photograph under the rubric of bathing beauties, but the photograph is not about scantily attired gals. It is about being alive. We know the photographer, like his subjects, is knee-high in the water and may be splashed any minute. The girl with the polka dot cap holds seaweed as gracefully as a wealthy woman handles her ruffled parasol. The girls' expressions come not just because it is summer and the sun is shining on them, but because of Nicholls' ability to bring out all the warmth and vitality in them.

Singing, drawing, dancing, reading aloud, winter sports, ball playing in the garden, photography and amateur theatricals were important parts of the Nicholls family's daily life. It was a loving, unpretentious, talented family that had the basic necessities and so felt grateful; the 'luxuries' would be saved for, shilling by shilling, and valued that much more. An open house every Sunday with lively conversation and a warm welcome is what all who knew Nicholls most vividly recall.

Vita Sackville-West did not describe such an idyllic picture of the aristocracy, the class she intimately knew. Her book *The Edwardians* chills the bone and is absolutely riveting. It reads like the insider account that it is. Sackville-West allows the central figure in the book, Sebastian, a young Lord, to describe his mother the Duchess:

> She is a famous hostess, with a talent for mimicry and a genius for making parties a success. She is charming and vivacious. In private life she is often irritable and sometimes unkind. She likes bridge and racing. She never opens a book, and she cannot bear to be alone.[7]

He concludes: 'Since we cannot have truth, let us at least have good manners.' But the conscience of the book, the explorer Anquetil (whose invitation to the house party has nothing to do with either money or breeding), just silently sighed before taking off to remote corners of the world:

> God help us, for surely no fraud has ever equalled it. These are the people, or a sample of them, who ordain the London season, glorify Ascot, make or unmake the fortune of small Continental watering-places, inspire envy, emulation, and snobbishness – well, thought Anquetil, with a shrug, they spend money, and that is the best that can be said for them.[8]

'Money,' said Anquetil; and 'manners,' said Sebastian – an unparalleled combination and the upper class knew it.

The Season was a necessity, not merely for marrying off one's daughters or reaffirming one's position in society but, as Priestley in his great wisdom reflected: 'The term "idle rich" was often seen and heard in those days. But in fact the rich were not idle at all. No matter how much money they may have, very few people can face empty days, months, years. . . .'[9] The Season helped pass the time. Plumptre remarks that house parties during racing events, were popular, although exhausting for the hostess, because at least they gave the guests something to do between meals. Priestley adds:

> It might be found that any society nearing the end of its high time, making hay while the sun still shines, overdoes everything. . . .
> Toiling away at pleasure, these drones and butterflies might as well

be worker ants . . . just below the conscious level, there was a vague feeling that the end was almost in sight, that their class was now banging away in the last act. So they overdid everything.[10]

'The Edwardian age,' writes James Laver, 'was probably the last period in history when the fortunate thought they could give pleasure to others by displaying their good fortune before them. . . .'[11] Conspicuous consumption, according to this line of reasoning, has a kind of benevolence about it. The aristocracy laboured long and hard to dazzle the proletariat and give off a glow that would lighten their subjects' lives. Since most people never came near the gentry, photographers like Nicholls performed a social function (if we are to continue along this line of asinine reasoning) beyond the recording of their age. They dispensed a tonic and a salve.

'The first decade of the twentieth century was for the English a decade of badly strained optimism,' wrote H. G. Wells. 'Our Empire was nearly beaten by a handful of farmers amidst the jeering contempt of the whole world.'[12] Nicholls had seen this first-hand. He had lived in South Africa since 1892, and when war broke out became the official photographer for the journal *South Africa* and contributed to the *Illustrated London News* and other publications. In a letter from South Africa to his wife in England, Nicholls quotes a former friend, 'old de Million', as saying the Boers were well prepared to fight:

> It's all very well for you fellows to think this matter will be decided in a month or so, & that one big battle will settle the matter, oh no. This business can as easily last years as months, & the one big battle you hope won't come off, we know we can't meet you men in open fight, & we are not going to try, you've got to find us all the time. . . . well we shall go on murdering one another until the Powers step in & say that there has been enough.[13]

In this new kind of warfare, Britain's enemies hid. They didn't play by the rules; they were unsportsmanlike. Even worse, Britain's moral mission had come into question. Nicholls witnessed his country's vulnerability and was determined to show, in his post-war work, a nation holding fast to its sportsmanlike values, its rituals, and its pleasant pursuits. Although there were wars, poverty, strikes and discord during this period, Nicholls appeared steadfast in showing a sanguine society. His Edwardian photographs were to be a contrast to the bloodshed and tedium he had witnessed during the Boer War. Humanity at play was to be his new theme.

The Liberals won the 1906 election and the period until 1910 has been called a 'brief but brilliant period of Liberal optimism'. Nicholls tried to give a visual coherence to this positivism. His was not a definitive view of Edwardian life; it was, like a summer holiday, a rest from what came before and would come immediately after. Nicholls' photographs of the Edwardian social scene are bracketed by his Boer War and First World War work. There is a radiance to the Edwardian era and to Nicholls' depiction of it. 'When it dined and wined, laughed and made love,' wrote Priestley, 'it had not yet caught a glimpse of the terrible stone face this world can wear.'[14] Its glow is all the more golden because of the dark chasm that followed.

There is a photograph of the 1907 Derby (page 18) in which every face is expectant and every heart, we know, is filled with hope. There are young lads and an old Indian and men in a wide range of head-gear and clothing. What they share is hope and a belief in luck, and no one could deny them their right to it. There are, in Nicholls' work, many pictures of working-class men who walked to the Derby from London, refusing to spend their money on a bus or train ticket when they could put it on a bet instead. In one picture (pages 22–3) they have their early morning wash from a communal bucket, and the surprise comes less from seeing someone decidedly better dressed than the others than from spotting a man with a peg leg who made the journey. Another picture (page 23) shows two young men who have fallen asleep along the route (others are visible in the distance), but who had the foresight to sleep with their hands in their pockets so they would not be robbed of their hard-earned pounds.

A young dandy at the Derby shows his palm to a gypsy fortune-teller and half believes what this woman, who could never hold his hand in any other circumstances, tells him (page 28). In subtle ways Nicholls' work is about the things that bind and the things that separate people. Money and manners, the outward signs of class, are divisive; hope, hunger, joy, jealousy, love, hate, competition and youthful rebellion are universals.

There is a lovely story about Queen Victoria imploring 'Bertie' (the Prince of Wales) to refrain from going to Royal Ascot on Wednesday and Friday and to follow family tradition by going only on the Tuesday and Thursday. She loathed his attraction to racing and wrote that his 'example can do *much* for good and do a great deal for evil. . . .' His reply was adamant. He wrote that he was 'past twenty-eight years old' and had 'considerable knowledge of the world and society' and wanted to attend Ascot each day with his friends. '. . . allow me to use my discretion in matters of this kind,' he firmly requested.[15]

> What is peculiarly Edwardian, making it a new age, is not the solid lump of conformity it carried over from Victorian England but the various challenges, denunciations, rebellions, all the attempts to break away from it, to push forward into a freer atmosphere. It is the new ferment and not the stiff old complacency that gives the age its character. Even King Edward himself, for all his limitations, was a new kind of king.[16]

One of the outward shows of this new freedom was dress, and indeed it was the Edwardians who brought fashion to the races. Extravagant clothes with fine lines are a blessing for a photographer, and Nicholls delighted in the new look. Cecil Beaton, who used Nicholls' photographs when designing the costumes and sets for *My Fair Lady* (without, incidentally, knowing the name of the photographer who had produced the gems), wrote: 'Fashions tend to extremes before being dropped, and the elaborate head-gear had now become like the last spurt of a Catherine wheel.'[17] The competition inside the Royal Enclosure was often as intense as that on the course.

> One of their dressmakers described these elegant women . . . as looking like fillies paraded for luxury. Competition made them achieve the impossible, since all the Parisian dressmakers outdid each other in invention and daring to assure the triumph of their latest creations. Sometimes on the very opening of a race meeting, dressmakers' assistants would be still sticking pins into a gown that was to be displayed that same day.[18]

In the paddock area at Royal Ascot, a woman's large red parasol frightened a horse, which then reared. She was heard to say, 'It's perfectly *scandalous* that horses should be allowed in here.'[19] There are many contemporary quotes that imply that Edwardian gentlemen actually preferred horses to ladies, or at least considered them on a par, so obviously there was no chance that ladies parading between races would *not* have competition for attention from four-legged, equally well-bred fillies.

To be admitted to the Royal Enclosure one had to meet the same prerequisites as for a court presentation. Inside that fence was a tightly knit club and they didn't need name tags, as they currently do, to confirm who they were. In those early years, each class had its own magnetic field; you were irrevocably pulled to your place in society. The laws of nature were seemingly infallible and you always ended up where you belonged. This 'bunching' of like individuals is highly visible in Nicholls' photographs – cloth caps are grouped with cloth caps, top hats with top hats, and so on.

To be in a traffic jam in a boat on the Thames seems eminently more pleasurable than to be in any other kind of traffic jam, and there is a lazy glaze over almost all Nicholls' Henley Regatta photographs. A soporific young man in a deck-chair (pages 76–7) is the subject of a beautifully composed picture. The background is soft, like a whisper; the empty deck-chairs like notes in a lullaby. Who would not want to be on the Thames on a warm summer's day in a straw boater or cotton dress, rocked by the rhythm of the waves and amused as much by one's neighbour balancing in a punt as by the rowers straining every muscle in their skiffs?

Nicholls' coverage of Henley has a sophistication that we tend to believe only appears much later in the history of photography. He shows us individuals, perfectly placed, at Henley station waiting for friends to arrive by train (pages 64–5) or at Phyllis Court, with its Japanese lanterns and tables laid for tea (pages 80–1). These men and women dress impeccably and walk with exquisite grace. More than in any of his other work, the women at Henley are sensual, whether lifting their dresses to their ankles to walk across the lawn (page 75), leaning over to share a few words with an admirer (page 76), lounging somewhat nervously in a punt or even when sitting somewhat awkwardly on the riverbank (page 68). Perhaps it's because the light, white dresses are so flattering to female curves. As for the men, they too seem more masculine as they are viewed from a distance rowing down the straight course or attempting to keep a punt in place. We cannot see the sweat, but we know it is there.

Royal Ascot, the Derby, Henley Regatta, Goodwood, Lord's and Cowes Regatta were about more, of course, than who won the race or the game that day. Each was part of a tradition; each had its familiar order that, like any set ceremony, gave comfort through continuity. But each, after order was established, threw certainty to the wind. No one knew, nor could know, who would win that day. The richness of each event lay in its ability to satisfy two opposite human needs – ritual and risk. They were also celebrations, whether of the more boisterous kind, as on the Downs at Epsom, or the more languid kind in a punt on the river at Henley, watching a day's cricket at Lord's or sharing a picnic in the grounds of Goodwood. On certain days, in the sunshine of the new century, civilization seemed to be doing just fine.

There is a series of photographs taken at the Derby in 1914 that hints that the golden summer is coming to a close (pages 40–1). Nicholls followed a group of jaded, wealthy sophisticates first perched atop their automobile watching the race, then sitting around the lunch table bantering. The weather is cooler than in previous years, the women need fur wraps; their expressions have hardened, they concentrate less on the track. We too feel a chill in the air. It is the image of these Edwardians having just finished lunch – wine glasses raised, crumbs on the cloth – cracking jokes and smoking their last peacetime cigars and cigarettes, that speaks directly to the emotions. The party is coming to an end.

1. Quoted in George Plumptre, *The Fast Set: The World of Edwardian Racing* (London: Andre Deutsch, 1985), p. 58.
2. Plumptre, *The Fast Set*, p. 58.
3. C. B. Fry, *Life Worth Living* (Eyre and Spottiswood, 1939) p. 386.
4. Roger Mortimer, *History of the Derby Stakes*, quoted in Godfrey Smith, *The English Season* (London: Pavilion Books, 1987), p. 70.
5. Plumptre, *The Fast Set* p. 171.
6. *Kodak Magazine*, June 1934.
7. Vita Sackville-West, *The Edwardians* (New York: Doubleday, Doran & Co., 1930), p. 27.
8. Sackville-West, *The Edwardians*, p. 11.
9. J. B. Priestley, *The Edwardians*, p. 57 (London: Sphere Books Ltd, 1972; first published William Heinemann Ltd., 1970).
10. Priestley, *The Edwardians*, p. 61.
11. James Laver, *Edwardian Promenade* (Boston: Houghton Mifflin Company, 1958), p. 4.
12. H. G. Wells, *The Wife of Sir Isaac Harman* (London: Macmillan, 1914), pp. 258–9.
13. Letter dated 9 August 1900 from Horace W. Nicholls at the Imperial Hotel, Martizburg, Natal to his wife Florence in England. Family Collection.
14. Priestley, *The Edwardians*, p. 57.
15. Plumptre, *The Fast Set*, pp. 46–7.
16. J. B. Priestley, *The Edwardians*, p. 84.
17. Cecil Beaton, *The Glass of Fashion* (Garden City, N.Y.: Doubleday, 1954), p. 85.
18. Beaton, *The Glass of Fashion*, pp. 71–2.
19. Plumptre, *The Fast Set*, p. 138.

Whenever Nicholls' own captions are known, they appear in quotation marks under the photograph. All other captions have been written by the author.

The Derby, 1907

THE DERBY

THE DERBY

As the great horse-loving statesman Lord Rosebery remarked,
"a roistering party [in 1779 and 1780] at a country house
founded two races and named them after their host [Lord
Derby] and his house [The Oaks]. Seldom has a carouse had a
more permanent effect."

GODFREY SMITH
The English Season, 1987

Fairgrounds. Derby Day, 1906

Asleep along the route to Epsom. Derby Day, c. 1910

Early Morning wash after walking from London to Epsom. Derby Day, 1906

The Derby, no date

The Derby, 1914

Number board. The Derby, no date

Lord Rothschild on horseback in paddock.
The Derby, no date

Lord Rosebery, the only Prime Minister to
have won the Derby (right) and Lord
Dalmeny studying the number board,
no date

Gypsy fortune teller at the Derby, no date

Watching the finish. Derby Day, no date

The Derby, 1913

The Derby, 1914

Photomontage depicting gypsy campsite at the Derby, c. 1906

Photomontage of religious gathering at the Derby, 1908

A sailor and friend picnic on the grass. The Derby, 1913

Lunch atop an automobile. The Derby, 1913

The Derby, 1913

The Derby, 1907

Vanderbilt lunch party. Derby Day, 1910

'After the Derby (A Rush for Crumbs which Fall from the Rich Man's Table)', 1908

'A Scene at the Course, Derby Day', 1914

Derby Day, 1914

In the paddock, Royal Ascot, no date

King Edward VII (*centre*) at Royal Ascot, no date

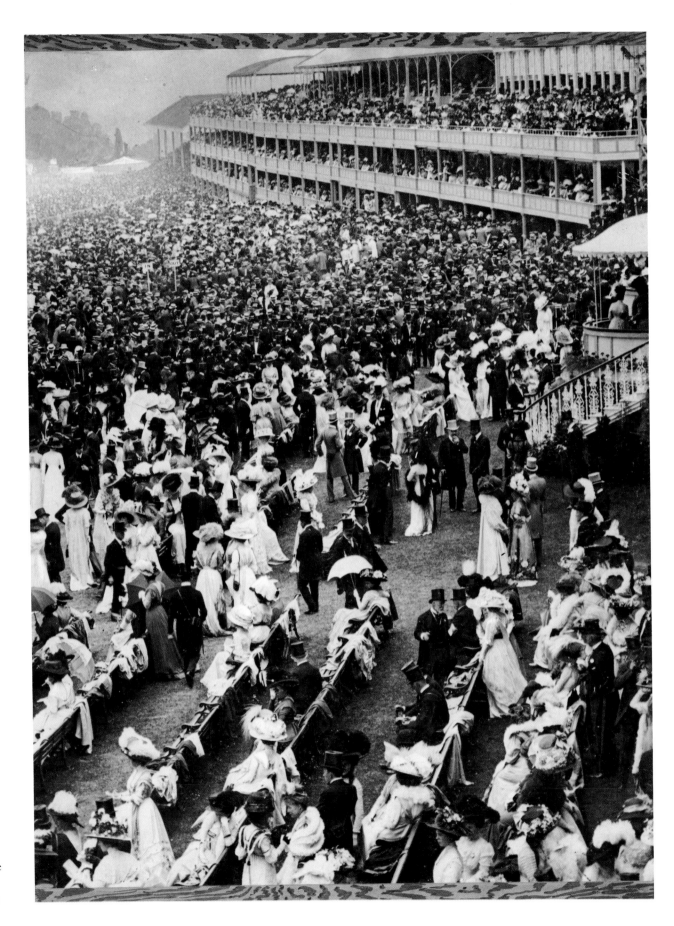

The Royal Enclosure,
Royal Ascot, 1909. The
Prince of Wales, later
King George V, centre

Royal Ascot, c. 1909

'Miss Marie Lloyd in the Paddock', no date

The Royal Enclosure, no date

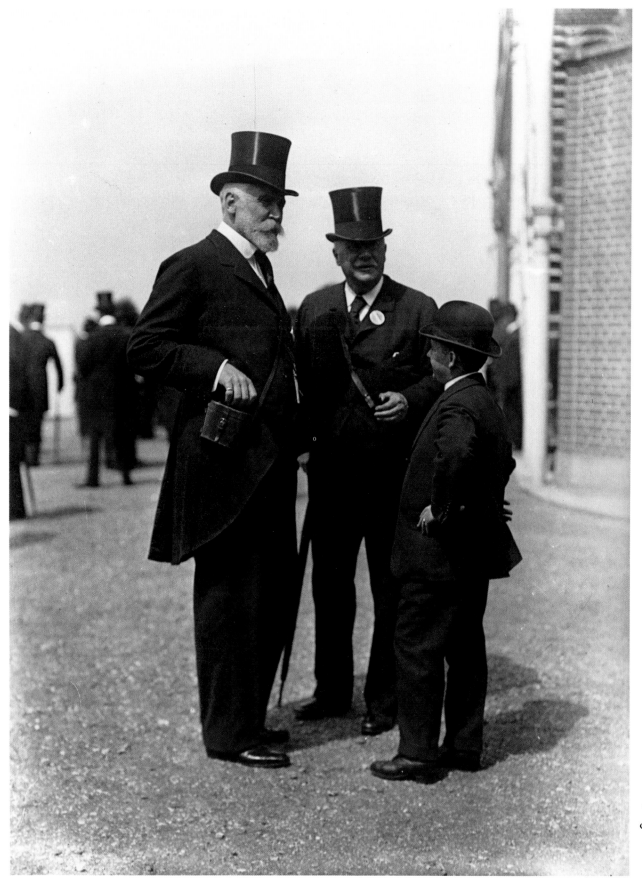

'Sir Edgar Benson (left)
chatting to Mr. Metcalfe
(racehorse owner)
& Jockey Plant.'
Royal Ascot, no date

'Mixed Humanity:
A Scene on a Race
Course in Merry
England (Ascot)',
no date

'Ascot, fashions', no date

Lord Lonsdale, top hat
and umbrella, studying a
runner. Royal Ascot,
1907

Royal Ascot, no date

Photomontage, heavily
retouched, made from
four photographs cut and
pasted together.
Royal Ascot,
no date

56

The Grand Stand in the Royal Enclosure,
King Edward VII in the Royal box, (centre),
c. 1906

BLACK ASCOT

*The most significant aspect of England's mourning period for
King Edward was the social event that came to be known as
"Black Ascot". At the first Ascot racing season after the popular
monarch's death, society appeared dressed from head to foot in
black. . . . Fashions tend to extremes before being dropped,
and the elaborate headgear had now become like the last spurt of
a Catherine wheel. These vast picture hats, perhaps set on one
side of the head and piled high with black ostrich feathers mixed
with osprey or black paradise feathers combined with black
tulle, were worn not only in mourning for a king but for a glory
that had gone for ever.*

SIR CECIL BEATON
Glass of Fashion, 1954

Black Ascot, 1910

Ascot, Sunday, Boulter's Lock, 1907

'Among the boats, Henley Regatta', 1904

HENLEY REGATTA

'Henley station', 1907

'Henley Week: Arrival of a special', 1907

Henley station, 1912

Henley Regatta, 1911

Phyllis Court, Henley, no date

Phyllis Court, Henley, 1908

'Henley, looking down stream', no date

Henley Regatta, 1911

Henley Regatta, 1907

The luncheon room. Phyllis Court, 1907

Walking towards the luncheon room. Phyllis Court, 1907

76

'A Popular Actor "Off Duty". Mr Cyril March under the trees at Phyllis Court, Henley', 1911

Henley Regatta, 1908

Henley Regatta, 1908

Henley Regatta, 1908

Henley Regatta, 1908

'Tea on the Lawn, Phyllis Court, Henley Regatta, Final Day', 1914

'Phyllis Court Banks looking downstream'. Henley Regatta, 1914

'The Occasion of Their Majesties' only
visit to Henley during Their Reign
showing the Procession of Boats and Royal
Barge coming up the famous Straight Mile
and receiving a massed Salute from the
Oarsmen', 1912

Lord's cricket ground, 1908

Society

LONDON SOCIETY

*Late afternoon in Hyde Park meant state carriages and
barouches, with beautifully dressed occupants, pulled up under
the trees. It was not etiquette to handle the reins oneself in the
afternoon so we sat on rows of chairs chatting and behaving as if
the world we knew, bounded by the Smart Set, was a fixed orbit,
as if London – our London – was a place of select social
enjoyment for the Circle, as if nothing could change in this best of
delightful worlds. . . .*

DAISY WARWICK
Memoirs

*In spite of our unpropitious climate, the [Rotten] Row, in Hyde
Park, remains one of the most distinguished places in Europe.
If the frocks are not as gay as some that are seen on the Riviera or
the Bois, London may fairly claim that nowhere are prettier
women to be seen. Scores of noteworthy people walk in the Row
every morning during the season and all sorts of persons, from
Secretaries of State to future Royal Academicians, to say
nothing of their womenfolk, make it a happy hunting-ground for
gossiping with their friends.*

BLACK AND WHITE
19 March 1910

Hyde Park, 1907

'The Famous Wall Game "Close Bully".
The Game which is played nowhere else
in the world but Eton College is the Great
event of St. Andrew's Day. . . . It is a
game which baffles description and may be
played for years without its intricacies
being mastered. Only two goals have been
made in twenty-two years.' Eton, c. 1908

Outside the entrance to
the horse show, c. 1909

Going to the horse show,
Olympia, no date

'His Majesty the King & Her Majesty the Queen at Olympia showing in foreground the assembly of Officers from all parts of Europe & America, Coronation Year 1911. Included in picture from left to right: Duke of York, Prince of Wales, Sir Gilbert Grenvall, Crown Princess of Sweden, Crown Princess of Germany, King George V, Lord Redesdale, Queen Mary, Crown Prince of Germany.'

Artist at easel in the stables at Olympia, no date

Goodwood, c. 1912

GOODWOOD

a garden party with racing thrown in

EDWARD VII

Goodwood, c. 1912

Lord Lonsdale, Called the Sporting Earl,
the Yellow Earl and Lordy, smoking the
six-inch cigar named after him. Goodwood,
c. 1912

Lord Marcus Beresford, the manager of
King Edward's stables (left), and probably
Alec Taylor, horse trainer (right).
Goodwood, no date

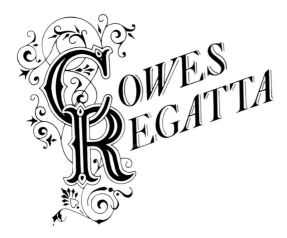

COWES REGATTA

Near the Royal Yacht Squadron, Cowes Week, 1912. 'It was easier to enter the House of Lords than to become a member of the Royal Yacht squadron.'

Below Photomontage made from four photographs cut and pasted together.
Cowes Regatta, 1910

Right Racing at Cowes Regatta, no date

'Waltzing in the Sea. A Novel Pastime for Bathers (Scene at Margate)', no date

At Sandown, Isle of Wight, no date

The Riviera

Carnival, Nice, 1912

THE RIVIERA

. . . one may confidently expect a special rush of visitors from foggy old England [to the Carnival and Battle of Flowers at Cannes, Nice and Mentone before Lent] glad indeed to deport themselves in the fantastic revelry King Carnival, to wade ankle-deep in confetti, to pelt each other with lovely blossoms of the Côte d'Azur, and forget there was such a thing as an Election.

BLACK AND WHITE
29 January 1910

Battle of Flowers, Carnival, Nice, c. 1908

Place Massena, Nice
c. 1911

Carnival, Nice, 1911

'A Corner of the Place Massena Nice. A Typical scene of Revelry on the last Sunday of Carnival . . . is portrayed in [this] composite photograph [Nicholl's term for photo-montage]. The Place Massena becomes a sort of night Theatre surrounded by boxes and tiered seats for those who wish to view the lively scenes without taking part.' c. 1912

*Sooner or later all the world was to be seen in the Rooms [at
Monte Carlo], in the Square or on the Terrace; though there I
never went because of the pigeon shooting.*

Mrs C. S. PEEL, OBE
Life's Enchanted Cup, 1933

'Lord Saville at the pigeon trap, Monte Carlo', c. 1908

'Pigeons in Casino Grounds, Monte Carlo', 1908

A family group taken by Arthur Nicholls, Horace's father (far right), at the family home, Newham Grove, Grantchester, on the occasion of his brother Henry's wedding. A separate negative was made of Arthur and then printed into the group portrait. The final print was subsequently retouched to hide the lines where the two negatives join. John Nicholls, Sr. and his wife (Horace W. Nicholls' grandparents) are seated on right. Charlotte (Arthur's wife and Horace's mother) is on far left. Reclining in front is Charles, the brother who reputedly squandered the family fortune. Albumen print, 1871.

WRITING A BIOGRAPHY of a photographer is analogous to looking through both ends of a pair of binoculars. Studying the pictures is like using the eyepiece: the pictures become larger than they were, and the longer one looks the more there is to see. To write about a picture one needs to spend time, read it like a short, sweet poem that has mystery and meaning far beyond the few chosen words that appear on the page. To lose oneself in an image is the only way to transcend the image, to enter the world of the immaterial as well as the actual. Truly, the image is enlarged.

But trying to find the individual who made the pictures is like using the wrong end of an optical instrument. Unless one is particularly fortunate in the extant documentation, the photographer's personality, instead of being magnified, becomes more and more elusive. One wants to discover a large (if not larger than life) individual. Photographs are so visual, so ready for interpretation. A life is really a closed book and it takes an enormous amount of prizing to see into it even slightly. There is a letter here, a remembrance there, some statistics, some dates and ever so many questions. How does one resurrect the creative mind, the passionate heart out of the few crumbs left after the banquet of an artist's life? One can quote sources, trace movements, look at portraits, and stare into space. In the end it is the work that matters after the life has been lived, and it is to the work that we must constantly refer.

A study of the life of an artist, however, does enrich the understanding of the work. Motivations, aspirations, passions and forces working on an individual become defined. A dance can be danced on an empty stage but when it is performed in front of a backdrop, connections appear that otherwise would not be made. A biography of an artist, brief or intensive is a backdrop to the work and makes for a fuller encounter with the art.

Horace Walter Nicholls was born on 17 February 1867 in Cambridge, the eldest son of Arthur Nicholls and Charlotte Johnson, both of Norfolk. His grandfather was John Nicholls, an architect, builder and restorer of cathedrals, churches and castles, including Dunster Castle in Somerset. The family home was Newnham Grove, Grantchester, Cambridge and they must have been prosperous, otherwise there would be no stories now about Arthur's elder brother Charles dissipating the family fortune.

Arthur learned photography sometime in the 1860s and by the 1871 census both he and his younger brother Henry were listed as professional photographers. Horace, therefore, had both a father and uncle who had become infatuated with the new field of photography, learned the complicated wet-collodion process and believed it a suitable profession for a young man. Little is known about Henry, but Arthur practised photography well into the twentieth century with studios first in Cambridge, then Sandown, Isle of Wight and finally in Reading.

For Arthur, a photographic negative and print offered the same creative potential as an empty canvas. A painter of still-lifes and portraits, he also painted on photographs in both oil and water colours. But his pride, and possibly his greatest source of income, were the type of photographs he called 'binographic' and 'triptographic'. On these, one person would appear in various carefully planned poses, often to extraordinarily clever effect. A Reading newspaper tried to put Arthur Nicholls' contribution in context:

> . . . The 'bino' has been a more or less ordinary photographic jest in a simple form for some time past. That is to say you could be seen in a photograph talking to yourself with a different hat on, or looking at your *alter ego* across a table. Mr. Nicholls' secret process goes far beyond this. One of his subjects is measuring his *doppel-ganger* for a suit. Another is leaning out of a window emptying a jug of water on herself as she lies asleep in the garden below. Another is looking at herself as she appears when she has been 'split' from her bicycle. The weirdest is looking aghast at his head as it floats bodiless in the air. Altogether it is a queer collection, well worth seeing.[1]

Horace learned photography from his eccentric father who instilled in his son a belief that a photographer, even a commercial photographer, was an artist. Arthur believed that using a camera was not a licence to forfeit one's imagination. Horace learned from his father that the camera gives one limitless creative potential and that what some call 'tricks' in photography can, with a clear aesthetic vision, or purpose, or wit, produce images of originality and value.

Horace's early years were spent in Cambridge as his father's studio was at Post Office Terrace where he had a thriving business taking portraits of collegiates. When Horace was about eleven the family moved to the Isle of Wight and by the age of fourteen he was an apprentice to his father whose studio was now at 17 High Street, Sandown. Horace was the eldest of nine children and although the family stayed in Sandown until the 1890s, Horace left home in about 1884 to become an apprentice to a chemist in Huddersfield. Whether this chemist was to teach him a new profession or whether the chemist also had a photographic business on the side, is not known. He never pursued any career other than photography.

Nicholls' daughters liked to refer to their father's *wanderlust*. While in Huddersfield he saw an advertisement in a newspaper for a young man to work for a photographer in Chile. He applied for the job and, according to his youngest daughter Peg, 'to his amazement a few weeks later a letter arrived offering him the job.'[2] Very few prints from this period remain: some anonymous sitters; a street scene showing the procession of Corpus Christi in

'Tierra del Fuegian Indians (Better class)'. Albumen print, c. 1887

Santiago; a composite of Chilean women's heads, and a group portrait of Tierra del Fuegian Indians. He kept three albums titled *Recuerdos de Chile* by Grabado Diaz I Spencer. The name of the photographer for whom he worked is unknown, but possibly Grabado Diaz I Spencer with his double-barrelled Spanish and English name could have been his employer. Peg recalled her father saying about his time in South America: 'Perhaps they were the jolliest years of my life – my happiest came with my marriage and my children.'[3]

When he returned to England in about 1889 he joined the Cartland Studio in Windsor. It was through his employer that he met his future wife, Florence Holderness, Cartland's cousin. The Holdernesses were bakers, supplying to Windsor Castle, and George P. Cartland held a Royal Warrant which allowed him to advertise himself as 'Photographer to Her Majesty the Queen'.

After about three years in Berkshire, Nicholls again grew restless, wanted a change, and decided South Africa was the next frontier. It was, in the 1890s, an attractive location for an ambitious, talented young man; and, after Chile, it may even have seemed a modest choice for someone of British origin soon to be married. A photograph of Johannesburg in 1889 shows it to be little more than a settlement, with acres of empty land between makeshift buildings. This panorama, subtitled by Nicholls 'The Romance of the Rand', was taken by James Goch, but printed and sold by Nicholls in later years.

James F. Goch had practised photography in South Africa since 1886, and in 1889 built a studio on Pritchard Street, Johannesburg. Whether he advertised in England for an assistant, or whether Nicholls approached him, is not known. But in September 1892 Horace Nicholls arrived in Johannesburg to join the Goch Studio.

A year later, Nicholls returned to England to get married. The *Windsor & Eton Express* for 14 October 1893 announced:

> *PHOTOGRAPHY:* As an example of what can be done in photography, Wm. Cartland has had on view an enlarged photograph 48″ × 36″ representing the market in Johannesburg as it appears at 6 o'clock every morning. It was taken by Mr. H. W. Nicholls, formerly assistant to Mr. Cartland and now engaged in Johannesburg. His marriage took place at All Saints Church on Wednesday [11 October], with Miss Holderness, eldest daughter of Mr. George Holderness, Peascod Street. Mr. Nicholls will sail with his wife for South Africa on 28th inst.

Nicholls became manager of the Goch studio on Pritchard Street in 1893. Between 1892 and 1893 the studio had moved from number 67 to larger premises at number 63. The business became known as 'Horace W. Nicholls, The Goch Studio', and with Nicholls' penchant for overstatement and self-publicity, he dubbed himself 'the Johannesburg Photographer'.

Life was kind for Nicholls in South Africa. He soon had a fine house, with servants, and his wife gave birth to a son, George, in 1894. With Nicholls' undoubted encouragement, his two brothers, Herbert Arthur (Bertie) and Stanley, then only seventeen, came out to South Africa in 1893. Stanley joined

Above Florence (Holderness) Nicholls by either Arthur or Horace Nicholls, c. 1893

Above right Horace W. Nicholls and Florence Holderness by Arthur Nicholls, probably at the time of their marriage, 1893

Below Studio portrait by Horace W. Nicholls of his children George and Gertrude. Johannesburg, c. 1899

Horace at the Goch Studio and later became a leading South African photographer, dying in Pietermaritzburg in 1970.

The essence of a professional portraitist's job is to shoot and sell, and Nicholls had little reason to keep copies of his prints. The examples of his portraiture that exist show him to be competent and sometimes flamboyant. There are examples of composite printing, multiple exposures on one negative and photomontage, such as the many faces of the Johannesburg Reform Committee tightly packed on a cabinet-size card. These 'tricks' he would have learned from his father, who loved creating visual surprises.

The gold and diamond mines were central to the economic life of the area and Nicholls enjoyed leaving the studio and photographing his surroundings in a straightforward, if uninspired manner. Architectural photography was never his strength, and municipal growth, no matter how rapid, did not have the immediacy that Nicholls longed for in his work. He took pictures around Johannesburg partly for the historic record but principally because he knew there was a market for them. He sold prints through his studio located in the centre of town and in 1896 produced a small paper-bound album of twelve photogravure images entitled *Johannesburg*. Included were pictures entitled 'Between the Chains' (the equivalent of the Johannesburg stock and commodity market); 'Commissioner Street'; 'The Mutual Building'; two views of 'Pritchard Street'; 'Risik Street'; 'Morning Market'; 'Gold Mine and Miners'; 'A Stamping Battery'; 'Boer Family Trekking'; Kaffir Woman & Children'; 'Johannesburg Today', and 'Johannesburg in 1889'.

The most disturbing and unbearably haunting pictures Nicholls took during his long career are a series of seven exposures of a naked black miner being searched for diamonds at the Kimberley mines. In all but one picture, black men carry out the investigation, looking for diamonds in nostrils, mouth, anus, between toes, etc. A white man in a bowler hat sticks something up the miner's

Above 'A Boer Family. The father is holding & proudly showing the frontispiece of a book called *The History of the Forebrekker*, a book which is held in great esteem by all Boers in fact [in] many houses this book together with the Bible forms the complete library', c. 1898

Right 'A Promising Young Boer & Proud Father. The way a young Boer is trained. He is frequently sent out with *one cartridge* in the early morning with which he is expected by his father to bring back his food for the day,' c. 1898

backside while black security officers and other workers casually stand around the courtyard watching the man, placed in front of a corrugated iron shack, be degraded and humiliated. Nicholls did not attempt to give dramatic composition to or intrude on what was going on. The miner going through the ordeal could have been a puppet on a string – except for the power with which he connected with Nicholls each time he turned towards him. The man in front of Nicholls' camera was stripped naked, his self-respect usurped, but no one could steal the look in his eyes that Nicholls dignified for ever. Perhaps he never made prints from these negatives, but neither did he destroy them. Perhaps, too, he asked himself why he took them.

Nicholls made a small number of photographs of black South Africans in their own villages. Faces fill the frame, sometimes smiling but more often quiet and composed. Nicholls took the pictures close up, at eye level, and the predominant feeling, whether consciously or unconsciously reached, was that of equality. In a society where the word was not even used, the pictures invoking this possibility seem terse and uncompromising. Except for the series discussed above and one cheesecake anomaly, the majority of portraits of black South Africans show strong, dignified people grounded in their own culture and not yet dislocated or violated. The pictures describe individuals, not types.

The year 1896 was marked with calamity, catastrophe and drama in Johannesburg. There was a political crisis, the Glencoe railway disaster which killed forty people, a dynamite explosion which killed or maimed 150 people, followed five days later by a great fire in a large store (opposite Nicholls' studio), a railroad accident involving an engine and eight trucks, an infestation of locusts and a drought. Nicholls photographed these extraordinary events happening around him and grouped them together in his second small book, *Stirring Events in Johannesburg 1896*. Nicholls described the contents as a 'Description and Views forming as complete a panorama as possible of the rapid succession of events which marked the opening of the year 1896'. Of the

African, c. 1899

eighteen photogravures, the three most striking images show the flight of women during the political uprising, the great fire of 24 February and the menacing presence of locusts swarming telegraph wires. He became a photojournalist almost without choice.

A diversion that would be developed and broadened in Nicholls' later career was that of taking his camera to horse-racing events. The meets had the punters and the hustlers, the ladies and their daughters, the owners and the jockeys and even more horses present than in his later, better known studies. Taken mostly in 1897–8, these pictures which today exist as glass stereo transparancies in the Bensusan Museum in Johannesburg, are winsome studies of 'types' in action.

Two months before the Boer War officially broke out in October 1899, Nicholls placed the following announcement in the local papers:

The Vital Question:
What shall we do with our wives and
families during the coming crisis?
To you who have decided to send them away,
HORACE W. NICHOLLS
The Photographer,
of Pritchard Street
would make the following suggestion:
Have a complete Family Group taken
before they leave.
To those men who have now been parted
from their families for some time and have
yet to be separated indefinitely, it will be
galling to find, when the reunion comes, that
you have gone out of the children's memory,
and this is all too frequent with young
children. This can be avoided by sending
them a new photograph of yourself, which will
also be a pleasant surprise to the wife.
Have this done while you can, by visiting
HORACE W. NICHOLLS, The Goch Studio
Pritchard Street

As Nicholls was renowned for his sense of humour, the 'indefinitely' may have been his idea of a joke, rather than a morbid sentiment. Yet, the seed was undoubtedly planted in many men's minds that getting a photograph of oneself before the outbreak of war was a matter of some urgency. The question Nicholls raised at the beginning of the advertisement was quite personal as well, for he sent his wife, son and infant daughter to the Cape for safety at about this time.

War was declared on 11 October 1899 and by the 23rd Nicholls was the official photographer for the London-based publication *South Africa*, described on the title page as 'A Weekly Journal for All Interested in South African Affairs'. This publication, which previously concentrated on advertising steamers, hotels, insect repellents, boarding schools, gold fields and closing gold prices, now had a war to cover and a commitment to publishing actual photographs of the conflict. By the end of the month he had a licence which read:

Mr. Horace W. Nicholls having signed the Declaration attached to the Rules for Newspaper Correspondents accompanying Troops in the Field, is hereby Licensed to act as Correspondent for the *South Africa* with the Force in [left blank]

'Maloo After the Race', South Africa,
9 April 1898

'Lord Ullin After the Dead Heat',
South Africa, c. 1897

'Have a weed Bobby', South Africa,
c. 1897

He is authorised to draw rations for himself and one servant and forage for one horse.[4]

Unlike a soldier in a combat unit, taking orders and staying with comrades, Nicholls description of his forays to the front seem quite unimaginable. He described his experiences at Ladysmith in a letter to his wife dated 1st November 1899 which was subsequently sent to his brother-in-law in Windsor and published in *The Windsor Chronicle*. He recounted how, fast asleep on the floor of a friend's hotel room just two days before, he heard the troops moving out, rushed to the street, hurried back to the hotel kitchen to fill his pockets with bread and granadillas, and then with a fellow correspondent 'proceeded on our way towards the sound of the artillery fire' . . . but after a mile and a half 'found we were making for the Boer position'. From Nicholls' own description he wandered around the periphery of battlefields, in and out of where shells were landing, half the time not knowing where he was, yet nevertheless kept quite 'cool' about his photography. He wrote: 'I took a photograph of them [British soldiers] in the act of firing, which, however, loses its artistic effect from the fact that there is no smoke from the rifles with cordite cartridges in use.' Later in the letter he discussed further attempts to get striking pictures:

> I found that I should not be able to get my general view from this position, so left and went down to where the 'Gordons' were laying awaiting orders, and asked them if anyone could direct me to our artillery, but none of them seemed to know the exact road, and here came an unpleasant experience because I could only follow the sound of the guns . . . So I started off on a very unpleasant walk over very rough ground, through bush and dongas, all alone, and after I had gone nearly three miles to the left, not knowing exactly where I might fetch up – reaching the top of a slight rise was relieved to see our ambulance train down in a valley and made my way straight for them, and on reaching them sat down (tired out) on one of the ambulance vans, to get a rest . . . I had not been sitting there more than five minutes, when whizz came a shell right into the ambulance train and killed one of the poor 'Doolie-bearers', not more than a stone's throw from where I was sitting.[5]

The *Natal Mercury* for November 8th carried a news item stating that Nicholls' series of fourteen views of the bombardment of Ladysmith were available for sale.

Nicholls was excellent at self-promotion, and his itinerary during the war years is best described by him in some of the catalogues he prepared to accompany the carbon prints he subsequently sold of the conflict.

Horace Walter Nicholls during the Boer War, c. 1900

'Military Balloon Ladysmith', Boer
War, 1899

Above 'Officers and War Correspondant
[Nicholls on left] in Commandeered
Boer House, Pretoria', 1900

Top 'British Officers use a Drawing
Room in Commandeered Boer House,
Pretoria, as a Bed Room', 1900

'Ladysmith, After Nicholson's Nek,
Boer War', 30 October 1899

'Tea Time in the Prison Yard', South
Africa, no date

... MR. NICHOLLS ... left the Golden City shortly before war was declared ... taking every point and incident of interest from Dundee to Durban. He was in Ladysmith during the early bombardment ... [and] managed, by merest chance, to get out of the town by the last mail train from Ladysmith, bringing all his negatives with him. He afterwards proceeded through Natal by way of Estcourt, Pietermaritzburg, and Durban; thence to East London ... and thence to Capetown. From here MR. NICHOLLS proceeded to England, and while there he had the honour of privately exhibiting his photographs to the Princess Christian of Schleswig-Holstein, at the special request of Her Royal Highness; also to Lady White, the wife of the Hero of Ladysmith. Before again leaving England, MR. NICHOLLS was specially privileged to attend in the Royal Quadrangle at Windsor Castle and there photograph the men of H.M.S. Powerful before Her Majesty the Queen, on their return from Ladysmith. He then again left for the front, and by command of the Chief of Staff, was permitted to proceed by way of Bloemfontein and Kroonstadt to Pretoria; he was there granted an interview with Field Marshal Lord Roberts, who complimented MR. NICHOLLS on his work and allowed some interesting photographs of himself to be made to add to the series.[6]

Nicholls did not see himself as the average war correspondent. Firstly, he believed his photographs had artistic and journalistic value:

... I should say that having so frequently heard the remark in criticism of the fine pictures (representing War Scenes) produced by our best artists, 'Oh' yes, it's a grand piece of work, but it is only the artist's imagination,' I have made it my great aim throughout the Campaign to produce a series of large photographs which would appeal to the artistic sense of the most fastidious, knowing that they must as photographs have the enhanced value of being truthful.[7]

Secondly, he was a showman and a businessman who could turn his pictures into a popular lantern slide show titled 'Fresh from the Front' and make a profit for both himself and the Lord Mayor's War Fund.

Nicholls brought his family back to England, arriving on 30 December 1899, and by February 1900 had set up the following speaking engagements:

Feb. 26	Victoria Rooms, Clifton
Mar. 1	Royal Albert Institute, Windsor
Mar. 7	Town Hall, Conway
Mar. 10	Great Hall, Tunbridge Wells
Mar. 13	Assembly Rooms, Bath
Mar. 15	London Hotel Assembly Rooms, Taunton

Mar. 16	Guildhall, London
Mar. 22	Drill Hall, Tiverton
Mar. 24	Eton
Mar. 27	Town Hall, Hawick
Mar. 30	Gilfillian Hall, Dundee
Apr. 2	Assembly Rooms, Malton
Apr. 3	St George's Hall, Bradford
Apr. 6	Public Hall, Hastings

Nicholls took out advertisements in the local newspapers before the lectures, and afterwards the papers gave him glowing reviews. He had become a well-known witness of the Boer War and a celebrity. He proved he could engage an audience with words as well as pictures, an unusual talent for a photographer.

In June Nicholls sailed for South Africa, leaving his family behind. Of the many letters he sent Florence during this period of separation, only one lengthy missive from Maritzburg dated 9 August 1900 remains in the family collection. It is an example of his 'voice': not the self-congratulatory voice of his promotional pieces or the business-like voice of his First World War correspondence; rather the gentle voice of a husband reaching out to his wife with words of encouragement, tenderness and news.

> . . . I explained to you in the letter I sent you from Elandsfontein the reason you must not sail yet, but as I believe the train that carried that letter was wrecked you may not have received it, so I will tell you again, it is briefly this lovey, you would not be able to go to Johannesburg if you came, & I don't want you to put up with the discomfort of living in Capetown. . . .
>
> You would naturally think that having been in Pretoria & Johannesburg I ought to know all the latest news, but it seems to me that the nearer one gets to the seat of military operations, the less one knows of what is really going on. . . .
>
> I stand in the street [Pritchard Street, Johannesburg] for a while & try to drink the whole scene, the buildings are all there just the same the streets are orderly, & the people are moving about, but where are all the old faces, I feel for all the world like Rip Van Winkle. . . .
>
> The boy told me that everyone has told him I was killed at Ladysmith, & I may mention this has been the general idea up here in Johannesburg & Pretoria among those to whom I am known. I have been greeted on several occasions in this way 'Halloa Nicholls old chap, I thought you were killed long ago. . . .'
>
> Of course I cannot see how much has been taken [from the studio] altogether without going into matters very carefully, but I think £50 will cover stolen goods, everything else is partially ruined with dust & dirt, however all the negatives seem to be left intact which is a big item. . . .[8]

On 7 September 1900 Nicholls arrived back in Southampton. He had photographed thousands of British soliders: officers on horseback and foot soldiers in squadrons. He had tried to depict the war, which was still raging, in terms of individuals and groups, on the move, at rest, caring for horses, maintaining equipment, burying the dead. A sense of weary waiting, movement from one desolate spot to another, and heat and dust are thematic. The work falls into two categories: hundreds of record shots to sell to the fighting men and their families; and studies that tried to describe the soldiers' daily experiences. One hundred and ten of the former were published as collotypes in a book titled *Uitlanders and Colonists who Fought for the Flag 1899–1900*, and the best of the latter were made into carbon prints and sold for between two guineas and 10/6. The market for these prints lasted ten years and proved a source of both professional and financial sustenance.

Nicholls stayed in England with his family, speaking at the Royal Albert Institute in February and probably building his reputation in other ways, until they all sailed for East London on 8 June 1901. Exactly one year later Nicholls photographed the Ceremony of Thanksgiving in Pretoria, marking the end of the ugly war. He became manager of Davies Bros. Studios in Johannesburg but he was not to remain there long. On 2 August 1902, Horace, Florence, George, Gertie and the infant Violet arrived in Southampton. He was too tired or disinclined to photograph Edward VII's coronation four days later.

Around this time he sued the proprietors of the publication *Golden Penny* for infringement of copyright. Nicholls had sold a photograph taken during the Boer War to the *Graphic* for one guinea under his licence for one time usage. The *Graphic* gave the photograph to its sister publication which then printed it in 86,230 copies, 82,230 of which were sold. As a legal precedent had already been established in 1895, Nicholls was awarded a 'coin of the realm', in this case one farthing, for each copy of the *Golden Penny* published. He received £89 11s. 8d., plus costs. Nicholls' action was significant in helping to establish a consensus among publishers that freelance photojournalists could not be exploited or their pictures pirated.

The pictorial press originated soon after the invention of photography in 1835. *The Illustrated London News* began publication in 1842, followed by *L'Illustration* (Paris), 1843, *Illustrierte Zeitung* (Leipzig), 1843; and the two United States publications *Frank Leslie's Illustrated Newspaper*, 1855, and *Harper's Weekly*, 1857. They all relied on a variety of printing processes from steel engravings to lithography to woodblocks predominating, as the latter could be printed with text. Photographs were often used as the basis for illustrations but could not be printed directly in the papers themselves due to the limitations of printing technology. Photographers who provided pictures to the press found that the subtlety of their photographs was lost in translation to another medium.

William Henry Fox Talbot, the inventor of photography as we know it, had laid the foundation for halftone reproduction in the 1850s with his photoglyphic engraving process. A screen was used to break up the picture into small units suitable for holding printer's ink. It was not, however, until 1873 that an actual halftone reproduction appeared in a newspaper. The New York *Daily Graphic*

. . . It is worthy of inspection, too, as being the first picture ever printed in a newspaper directly from a photograph. There has been here no intervention of artist or engraver, but the picture is transferred directly from a negative by means of our own patented process of 'granulated photography'.

There was not another example in a newspaper of this innovation until 1880, and even then it was an isolated instance.

The problem for newspapers was speed. In the 1880s it took at least three days to get a halftone made. The expensive art journals and illustrated books which were not working to tight deadlines could wait for their illustrations to be ready. But the newspapers could not. In the early 1890s the halftone process became a commercial viability and, instead of days, newspapers could have their halftones made in hours.[9]

Between 1892 and 1893 halftone printing began to take over wood-engraving in the *Illustrated London News*[10] and magazines such as *The Strand*, *The Windsor*, *The Westminster* and *The Idler* came into existence, wedded almost exclusively to the new technology. Photographs just by themselves or groups of photographs around a selected theme were enchanting to the readers. A new career opened up for those willing to take the risk of leaving the more secure photographic professions such as portraiture and head for the streets, the battlefields and the unknown.

Thus, the 1890s saw the beginning of photojournalism as a profession, and Horace Nicholls was among the first to choose this career which always had about it an aura of adventure, social awareness and solid reporting. Nicholls had entered the field in 1896, when proximity to events gave him a unique opportunity to cover a series of disasters in Johannesburg.

The illustrations of the Boer War that appeared in the popular press were divided in roughly equal proportions between photography and drawing.[11] Nicholls established a reputation as an ace photojournalist. He also learned how to hustle and promote himself, make contact with art directors and editors, and how to produce pictures that would have an edge over the competition.

Upon his return to Britain, having the security of a steady sale of Boer War photographs, an established name and a great deal of personal charm, and possibly some inherited money, Nicholls set out to succeed as a freelance photojournalist. Week after week the photographs with his byline attest to the fact that he had no desire to be eclectic. He wrote: 'The chief aim of my work in photography is pictorial effect in preference to photographing anything and everything.'[12] He did not photograph political events or politicians, matinee idols or up-and-coming starlets, fox-hunting or football or follow royalty through their ceremonies and meandering. 'The Season' was his constant annual theme but he also had to earn a living during the rest of the year. Unlike most early photojournalists who went out to cover the news, Nicholls always tried to stay away from the 'pack' of cameramen and create his own stories or give visual coherence to small events he read about in the newspaper.

Above left HWN with his Newman & Guardia Reflex camera of about 1903. The lens was mounted in such a way that Nicholls' subjects often did not know they were being photographed

Above centre HWN with bicycle and camera. He frequently used a bicycle to go to events

Above right HWN perched precariously at Henley

Left HWN on scaffolding to get a better view

Right HWN in the studio at top of his house in Ealing. In the picture can be seen sky lights, printing frames, a seamless paper backdrop and a large studio plate camera

In these early years of photojournalism, photographers without ingenuity were relegated to the picture agencies, but resourceful ones like Nicholls could succeed as independents. Nicholls could sell, for example, a stunning picture of trees taken for his own pleasure, because he linked it to a pre-war article he had read in *The Morning Post* which discussed trees as an asset and their value in national defence. When Kitchener was promoted to Field-Marshal, Nicholls got out his old South African negative, printed it on a different background, and sold it to the press. Survival as a freelance photojournalist was precarious, but Horace Walter Nicholls had the right mix of talent, confidence, energy and imagination.

Normally Nicholls would choose his subject and then take a series of pictures that covered all the most interesting aspects of it. His intention, whenever possible, was to get the publication to use at least one image full-page, or even sometimes double page, and the others as smaller inserts in and around the main image. This would give the readers more to look at and provide Nicholls with extra earnings as he was paid per picture reproduced. He aimed to get his work into the same spots that the journals reserved for reproductions of works of art. In other words, he set out to make 'studies', as they were then called – pictures that people were expected to look at carefully, not just glance at. He wanted the readership to sit up and take notice of his pictures. Over and over again the only photographer to be given a full page would be Horace W. Nicholls. Words like 'A Camera Study', 'An Admirable Photographic Composition', 'The Art of the Camera: Studies by . . .', 'Photographs specially prepared by . . .' or 'A Remarkable Camera Study by . . .' would appear along with his name and a compelling caption. Herbert Ponting, who accompanied Captain Scott to the Antarctic (1910–12) and was himself an internationally respected photographer, wrote to Nicholls in 1914 in reply to a letter Nicholls had sent him:

> . . . I can assure you that there is no one from whom I would sooner have such a letter than yourself, as I have been a great admirer of your own work for many years – The splendid composition and your wonderful eye for a picture and the little things such as most people miss which constitute the very essence of life.
>
> Over and over again, when I have seen your pictures in the papers, I have been struck – not only with your wonderful ability and technique – but with your splendid judgement in the selection of your subjects. Knowing all this so well as I do, you will know how great a pleasure it has been to me to receive your letter.[13]

Among the journals and newspapers Nicholls contributed to were: *Black and White, The Daily Sketch, The Daily Mirror, Illustrated London News, Penny Pictorial, South Africa, The Bystander, The Illustrated Sporting [and Dramatic] News, The Graphic, The Referee, The Sphere, The Sunday Companion, The Tatler, The Times* and *The Guardian*. The art director of *The Times* was a close friend. On the back of each print he sent to the publications was stamped:

Above HWN keeping accounts and waiting by the telephone for an assignment
Below HWN setting off for Fleet Street with a portfolio of recent prints to sell to the newspapers and journals

Above 'The Last Homecoming', Edward VII's coffin brought to Windsor Castle, a photomontage made from two photographs pasted together which radically falsify perspective, 1910

Below One of the pictures used in 'The Last Homecoming'

This copyright photograph is supplied for reproduction in one issue only of the Journal specified in my account if acknowledged to "HORACE W. NICHOLLS" at foot of each impression for a fee and size as at foot. If published oversize or not acknowledged extra fee will be charged.

The acceptance of the photograph is an agreement to pay the fee whether the photo is used or not.

Fee 10/8 up to 6″×4″; 21/- up to 9″×6″.

Royal photos were a minimum of 21/-. Although there is no surviving evidence of his income, such as account books, Nicholls probably tried to earn about seven pounds a week which would place him firmly in the Edwardian middle class. This is based solely on the salary of £350 per annum he asked for when he joined the Ministry of Defence during the First World War.

Nicholls would carefully plan each day. If he read 'the King will Entertain his Royal Visitor at Windsor Castle next week,' he would look through the previous year's files to find a picture of Windsor Castle to take to a newspaper office. Or, again using Windsor Castle as an example, if he read about the proposed building of flats near the castle, he would pull out exactly the same picture, but this time find another photograph in his files that showed new flats, print it, cut it up, paste it onto the Windsor Castle print, mount it and write an arresting caption to do with Windsor before and after the proposed new housing. Probably, however, he would try to sell two prints rather than just one, and mount the original photo of Windsor showing how it then looked alongside the collage. Once he had his 'news item' he would change his clothes, place a flower in his lapel, put on his bowler, get out his cane, place his portfolio under his arm and catch a bus or the underground from his home at 9, Amherst Avenue, Ealing, to Fleet Street.

Another day he may have read about the 'church where Swinburne will be buried today' and hopped on his bicycle to get a picture of the church in time for that week's editions. Publications in the Edwardian period liked to have exclusives, and this policy suited Nicholls. Photographers such as Nicholls who did all their own developing and printing could never produce prints in quantity quickly or compete on the big news stories with agencies such as Topical, Sport & General, Illustrations Bureau, London News, Half-Tones, Graphic Photo Union or World's Graphic Press. Nicholls' aim was to make one print of a subject he hoped no one else had, and get it to the newspapers as quickly as possible. When his daughter Peg was old enough, he often had her go down to Fleet Street for him, but he never became an 'enterprise'. Once a print was chosen by the art director, Nicholls would be paid whether it was used or not. Rarely did Nicholls leave prints on approval.

Nicholls was best known for seasonal pictures, and when the Season was not buzzing, he would depict the spirit of summer, winter, autumn and spring with sometimes hackneyed, but often quite stunning, studies. Ice skating and tobogganing; building sand castles and donkey rides; harvesting and sowing all appear in the folders he labelled by category and kept on hand. An article he spotted about the reducing of coast-guard staff and the dropping of standards could result in a spate of bearded, hearty 'old salt' types. Out of context, the images often appear purely pictorial and without newsworthiness. Nicholls' genius as a freelance photojournalist was to never lose sight of the principle that every picture needed an angle, and normally a topical one, in order to sell.

He loved to travel and spent much of his time abroad. In January he might be at Mont Blanc, in February and March in Nice and Monte Carlo, but come May, June, July and August he was always back home for Ascot, Derby, Henley, Lord's, Goodwood and Cowes.

If a picture of Cowes could be improved by the addition of a few birds flying in the sky or an extra wave, then with scissors and glue he put it in. Nicholls frequently made photomontages, but was inconsistent about mentioning the fact in the caption. The newspapers had no policy on the matter and may well not have cared. If a hundred bodies jammed together was amusing, then five hundred bodies within a single frame was even more visually striking. Increasing population density was never a problem for Nicholls. To emphasize that on one rainy Derby there were umbrellas everywhere, he cut out strips of umbrellas and filled in all the empty spaces in one of his pictures, so that for as far as the eye could see there were black billowing shapes. An illustration from the 17 September 1910 issue of *Black and White* was captioned 'The Simple Life: A Study of the Simple Life as it Really Is – A Very Different Thing from the Holiday Picnics Affected by the Rich'. It shows a group of gypsies eating at the edge of a forest. The picture was so skilfully composed that no one reading *Black and White* would suspect any trickery, but the gypsies were photographed at the Derby and the trees came from another negative.

Nicholls may have believed that five bits of 'truth' pasted together added up to a higher truth, not a falsehood. Nicholls would argue, in the case of the gypsies by the forest, that there was nothing false in the statement he was

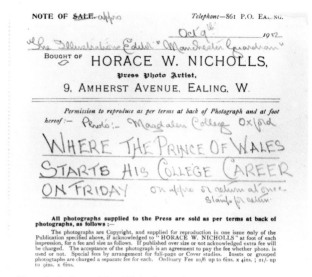

Above Label used by Nicholls on back of prints in conjunction with his stamp

Right Ice skating, c. 1909

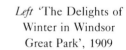

Left 'The Delights of Winter in Windsor Great Park', 1909

Left 'Aero Skiing in Chamonix. Son of Ferdinand de Lesseps of Suez Canal Fame – Count Bertrand de Lesseps has first constructed a wonderful air propelled machine which is capable of attaining a speed of anything from 25 to 80 kilometres an hour . . . or if snow fails, wheels can be affixed . . . when a much greater speed is possible even up to 100 miles per hour.'

trying to make. He had something to say at that moment about class differences, and it was far more important to him (and his livelihood) to get an image printed in the press that conveyed his meaning than to wait until chance dictated that the correct components would come together in a pleasing composition.

Nicholls had spoken of artistic licence, and he felt that he wanted the same freedom as an artist to make powerful, aesthetic statements. Photography is always linked to technical considerations. Nicholls did not have the tools that contemporary photographers have – flash, high-speed film, automatic focus, wide-angle lenses – so he used his ingenuity. Is using a wide-angle lens more truthful than Nicholls pasting two photographs together to form a panorama? Is photographing from an aeroplane that much more valid than trying to suggest with the means at his disposal the numbers of people at a gathering like the Derby? For Nicholls, photographic truth had a different meaning from what it has today. Now the public demands that the pictures in the press not be tampered with or altered in any way. Readers might question the written words, but they want to believe implicitly in what they see.

Nicholls wanted to give faithful representations. When technical constraints or bad luck prevented him from making the picture that he felt was the strongest statement, he used his imagination, wit and creative ability to get the result he wanted. Most of his photographs are 'straight', but many of his most fetching are montages. He believed pictures in the press should have aesthetic impact. His readers felt that any photograph, even one retouched (as was so common) or made from more than one negative, was much more 'real' than the illustrations they had always known.

In July 1914, when war was imminent yet still undeclared, three children in Ealing wrote to the Czar of Russia:

July 31st 1914

Your Majesty the Tzar,

We are just three little English children, who are writing to you to ask you to proclaim peace & not war. We are sure that you can do it if you like. War may not be so bad for Russia, but it is awful for England, because our food supplies may get stopped & that would be terrible.

Please do say "Peace", we are sure you will be kind enough, & you are so like our own king.

From

Violet
Sidney Nicholls
Peggy

Nicholls' original photograph which he printed at least six times. The prints were cut up to make final photomontage of rainy day Derby, c. 1906 (*right*)

George Nicholls' grave in Arras,
northern France, visited by his parents
in 1919.

The letter got as as far as Germany and was held there during the whole of the Great War. On 20 July 1920 it was returned to the Nicholls home, undelivered and unheeded.

The letter is one small yet significant detail that helps ascertain the character of the Nicholls family. Confident, caring, creative and somewhat unconventional, the children were undoubtedly encouraged by their parents to post their message. Nicholls himself kept it among his momentoes.

War was declared shortly after the letter was posted. George, the eldest son, who then was working in Germany as an apprentice to an engineering firm, returned home and immediately enlisted. Under age, he sought, and received, the consent of his parents. The family album for 1914 focuses on George looking dapper in uniform, showing a gun to his brothers and sisters, saying his farewells, proud to be 'a man'. Nicholls ends the album with a quote from Shakespeare:

> What's Brave,
> What's Noble
> Let's Do It.

The 1919 family album also begins with a picture of George, and the words 'Ever in our memory', and goes on to say, 'Just one of the Patriots who made Peace Possible.' The 1919 album is in a different key to the other albums which are filled with joyous memories. There is one picture in it that transcends the particular and becomes a universal. It is of George's grave at Arras, the sun breaking through the clouds, the weeds cradling the cross with its inscription that reads, 'KILLED IN ACTION'. This album ends:

> We are the Dead.
> To you from failing hands we throw
> the torch.
> Be yours to hold it high
> If you break faith with us who die
> We shall not sleep.

It was difficult for Horace Nicholls to have a son at the front and to be secure at home. He still envisioned himself as a war correspondent, although at the outbreak of the Great War he was 47 years old and too old to be with the combat troops. It is not known exactly what Nicholls did between 1914 and 1916. A letter dated 7 September 1916 to the Department of Information shows he was persevering in his attempts to obtain an official appointment and be sent abroad.

His frequent contacts with the Department of Information made them very aware of his acute desire to use his camera in the war effort and eventually he received a commission. A memorandum by Mr Ivor Nicholson of the Propaganda Department on 26 June 1917 read:

For some time since I have been here, I have been in touch with Mr. Horace W. Nicholls, an expert photographer, who was sent out in the South African war as an official photographer. I am confident that this gentleman is fully qualified to act as our own photographer. At present he is the substitution officer in Hounslow of the National Service Department. As he has not been in this position long, and in view of the fact that photography has been his work all his life, I do not think we should have much difficulty in getting the National Service Department to release him from their employment.

I have discussed the matter tentatively with Mr. Nicholls and have ascertained that we could secure his services for £350 a year. To begin with, Mr. Nicholls could develop his negatives in his own dark room, but later on I hope that we should be able to fix up a dark room here and all the printing of the negatives could be done by the photographic agencies in Fleet Street. Except in special circumstances the pictures would not be released to the British Press, as this might create a certain amount of friction with the photographic agencies.[14]

'British Universities in War Time. Cambridge. Clare and Trinity Tennis Courts,' c. 1917

The salary was questioned as 'out of proportion to those already paid to administrative officers'. Senior officials wanted confirmation that there was indeed enough work to employ one full-time person. But subsequent memoranda outlined duties and it became clear that the Department of Information was inundated with requests for propaganda-type photographs that they were unable to fulfil without a staff photographer.

A series of twelve illustrated books to be published in America was already being planned before Nicholls' appointment. Besides the proposed books, the main purpose of an official photographer would be to cover home front activities such as 'reviews of troops by the King . . . visits of prominent people to munitions works, hospitals and so on, and to fulfil any picture requests the department received from foreign countries. There were requests from the United States war office for example, for photographs of American troops being entertained by friendly Britishers, or pictures of Irish fighting men.

By 7 August 1917, Horace W. Nicholls was Official Photographer to the Department of Information and the stated brief was to take 'photographs in Great Britain for publication in neutral and Allied countries for propagandist purposes; he is exclusively attached to this Department, and the photographs he takes are the property of the Department.'[15]

Once Nicholls secured the necessary passes and permits, which, even in his official capacity, were not easy to obtain, he set off around the country on one assignment after another. He no longer had the opportunity to generate his own stories, but following other people's briefs allowed him a certain kind of creative freedom. His main concern was with making forceful images, not the marketplace. His photographs during wartime, unlike the modern conception of propaganda, were unmanipulated, straight photographs. What constituted a 'propaganda' photograph then was quite nebulous, and although Nicholls was told what to photograph, he was never told how to photograph it. Nicholls, by this time in his career, felt he knew more about picture-making than his superiors in the Department of Information, and if he had been trying to please someone other than himself, his photographs would not be half as powerful. Jane Carmichael, Keeper of Photographs at the Imperial War Museum, provided insight into what propaganda meant at the time in an article on the home front photography between 1914 and 1918:

> At the outbreak of the First World War propaganda was seen in terms of the presentation of the Government case to neutral, allied and enemy countries and not as something for home consumption. For much of the war the Government viewed propaganda as the means of influencing key figures abroad, not in terms of influencing the masses at home. The morale of the people was taken for granted and in view of the massive response to the first calls to arms this attitude seemed justified. It was only later in the war as the supplies of both men and munitions began to run short that the response of the civilian population began to concern their leaders, hence the emergence from a morass of ad hoc committees in late 1916 of a more defined body responsible for propaganda, the Department of Information. It gained full ministerial status in February 1918.[16]

Nicholls obviously had to think about 'propaganda value' even if it was unclear what it meant exactly and he accepted censorship as necessary in wartime. He found it loathsome, however, when he was thwarted from using his discretion

Below left 'Munition workers in one of England's great shell filling factories, Chilwell', 1917

Below 'Launch of a Standard Ship from a ship yard in Sunderland', 1918

at the time of photographing as a letter to a superior at the ministry attests:

> I was to-day called up on the 'phone by the Intelligence Officer of the Eastern Command, to attend at his office with my Permit Book. It has come about in reference to the two photographs I recently made on a Farm in Suffolk, entitled "THE HARVESTERS OF 1918", (a mixed group in which were included four German Prisoners). It occurred to me that they might be valuable Propaganda, which was my object in taking them. The Press Bureau were evidently of the same opinion, for I understand the photographs have been passed for Propaganda purposes in Germany, though stopped for publication elsewhere.
>
> The Intelligence Officer stated that I had violated the terms of my Permit in taking the photographs . . . and pointed out that my Permit Book said that among certain things that may not be photographed without Special Permission, the words 'Prisoners of War' appear. . . .
>
> I ought to point out that, had I started my journey with the object of photographing Prisoners of War, it would have occurred to me that a Special Permit ought to be obtained to facilitate my work, but the object of my journey on this occasion, was to photograph Woman in her varied War Activities, for which no Special Permit was necessary, and while busy with this work, the opportunity of photographing the group of Harvesters in question presented itself, and I felt that it should not be missed in all the circumstances, so took the photographs, and on my minute to Mr. Adams, when handing in the negatives, said that they should be submitted to the Censor.
>
> I am afraid my inclination would always be to secure a photograph which might prove of value to the cause, rather than risk losing it by waiting for a Special Permit, and then leave it for the Censor to decide, but as I understand it since my interview with the Intelligence Officer, I must use no discretion of this nature.[17]

The photographs taken between 1917 and 1918 are some of the finest of his career. Freed from finding his own subjects, he concentrated on the pictorial possibilities inherent in each assignment. Thus, going to the Chilwell shell factory, for example, he immediately framed his pictures to present a landscape of shells punctuated with people seemingly growing out of the unnatural terrain.[18] He saw the launch of a standard ship from a shipyard in Sunderland in abstract terms. An overriding sense of power results from the vigorous lines.

Surrealism, too, comes to dominate much of his work from this period. Because sending young men off to war is, ultimately, incomprehensible, Nicholls' photographs of men having medical examinations in order to be 'fit' for cannon fodder, can only be dealt with in terms of surrealism – for surely it cannot be reality. When Nicholls photographed the men back from the front,

'Enlistment – Medical Examination of Recruits No. 4 the eyesight test', c. 1917

'The patient examining the mould of his own face.' 3rd London General Hospital, where the sculptor Captain Derwent Wood, RA, designed facial moulds to disguise wounds

Above 'The electric trolley driver for luggage and mails at Liverpool Street Stn. G.E.R.', 1917–18

Above right 'The Woman Grave-Digger [Mrs. Kitchener]', 1917–18

Right 'Placing girl in muzzle of great naval gun to clean rifling', 1917–18

'War Office Supervisor, and indoor and
outdoor messenger', 1917–18

blown apart and waiting their turn for new eyes, noses, ears and limbs, and gave his pictures titles such as 'Repairing War's Ravages: Renovating facial injuries', we again know we are in a state of suspension – the pieces don't fit together but someone is trying to pretend that they do. Although photography is supposed to be the supreme master of reality in the visual arts, it is in fact, equally well suited to surrealism, super-realism and hyper-realism. The dismemberment of the body is a constant in surrealist art. No wonder some of his First World War photographs should come under this heading.

Nicholls will always be remembered as the photographer who captured the moment in history when women walked out of their homes and into men's jobs. The combination of a seemingly thorough investigation, a simplicity of approach and a brilliance in perception make his 'women at war' photographs one of his most profound contributions to the history of photography.

The idea to do the study initiated late in 1917. Nicholls' pass from the Secretary of the Ministry read: '[that] the bearer of this letter, is visiting the various centres of women's war activities for the purpose of obtaining a series of photographs, illustrating women's work in war time.' Most of the communication on the subject was between Nicholls and the Honorable Secretary of Women's Work Sub-Committee, Miss Agnes Conway. The Women's Work Committee was one of a number of groups set up to collect items for the proposed Imperial War Museum. Nicholls, in a letter to Conway, referred to her 'scheme' which was threefold. The immediate objective was to obtain sufficient pictures for an exhibition on the subject of women's war work to be held at the Whitechapel Galleries in the autumn of 1918. The more far-reaching goals were to document a seminal shift in the perception of women's capabilities and their massive contribution to the war effort. For this purpose, Nicholls was provided with lists of women's names, their occupations and addresses.

A 'Woman Coke Heaver' with a large sack on her back and 'The Woman Grave Digger' with a spade and pick over her shoulder are gritty, textural images. These two women are too tired to take a pose. Nicholls does not even try to get them to put on a smile for the camera, as was his natural inclination. He recognized the severity of their situation: families to care for, their husbands' businesses to run, loved ones at the Front. He just lets them be, and pays tribute to their strength.

Often Nicholls set up an 'action' type picture: a woman tram driver, a river postwoman in her boat, house painters, woodcutters, factory workers, carters, and so on. The action is set, the positions frozen, and the exposure made. These location pictures fall into two categories. In one group Nicholls tried to capture youthful optimism – wide-eyed, energetic women prepared to go to any lengths to perform their jobs well. He carefully lit and composed these pictures to give these women 'star' quality.

The other group of 'action' pictures is comparable to the opening of a play when the curtains part and on stage, perfectly positioned and absolutely frozen, is the chorus. In these pictures, he adopted the role of director, staging his picture carefully to create an overriding sense of harmony. He leaves the viewer convinced that immediately after the exposure, all the women will break into song, woeful or spirited, but sung with one voice.

More cerebral, more haunting than any of these are the images of one, two, or three women in front of nondescript backgrounds, sombrely dressed, doing nothing except look back at the photographer. Instead of tools they seem to hold thoughts, and to carry their load of apprehensions as visibly as the sack of coke. As in the work of great master photographers such as Nadar and August Sander, Nicholls proves once again that often the most straightforward portrait carries the greatest intensity.

Although his photographs of women are his best-known work from the First World War period, he carried out all types of assignments. His experience of photographing crowds during the Edwardian period helped him produce some outstanding shots of workers in factories and shipyards. Like Weegee, he seemed to have the knack of getting hundreds of people to light up their faces when he counted to three. He made memorable pictures of children waiting at the gate of a shipbuilding yard with dinner for their relatives, artists training for service in front of the Royal Academy, and British universities in wartime. And he was there to document the service at Winchester Cathedral on 11 November 1918 to solemnize the cessation of hostilities.

In December the Ministry of Information officially became the Imperial War Museum, and Horace Nicholls was asked to remain on the staff. His role was to head the darkroom and be responsible for the care, preservation and rephotographing of deteriorating negatives from all the fronts of the Great War. His 2,300 negatives of the home front were part of the archive. In 1932, fifteen years after Nicholls joined the Department, *The Sunday Dispatch* for 1 May 1932 ran an article that read: 'The guardian of 100,000 photographic negatives at the Imperial War Museum and 100,000 memories of all parts of the world has retired.'

Even during his years as a civil servant, Nicholls worked freelance for newspapers and journals. His published pictures from the twenties and thirties, however, have for the most part lost their edge, offering fewer visual surprises, less emotional impact and individuality than his earlier work. He

'The Water Gardens, Brighton.'

Two photomontages using some of the same negatives reversed, c. 1920s

photographed mostly during his holidays abroad, frequently recording the delights of snow-covered landscapes or hot Mediterranean promenades for the English in their temperate climate. Nicholls' livelihood no longer depended on being the best photojournalist in the business, and his pictures became 'softer'.

During his early freelance years Nicholls was described as 'working all the time', and he did rise to the top of his profession. During the First World War he was under constant pressure to produce and forced to travel a great deal. In the period between the world wars, however, he could devote himself to the children, all of whom lived at home until 1930. Everyone who knew Nicholls cites his great love of young people, his ability to captivate children and play with them for hours. They all comment, too, that his family life was of utmost importance to him.

George (1894–1917) had been killed in the war. Gertrude (Nicky) (1897–1979) trained as a nurse, never married, and was a sister at Great Ormond Street Hospital for Sick Children. Violet (b. 1901) attended Bedford College, became a schoolteacher, married Selby Hughes and has one adopted daughter, Lorna. Sidney (1903–1978), after a brief period at art school, was apprenticed to a tailor in Maddox Street, but always preferred the theatre. He and his younger sister Margaret (Peg) (1904–1985) starred in many amateur theatrical productions, and eventually Sidney became the well-known actor Anthony Nicholls, playing opposite Ivor Novello in 'The Dancing Years' at the Theatre Royal, Drury Lane, and acting with the Old Vic, the National Theatre and the Royal Shakespeare Company. His second marriage was to the actress Faith Kent, and their two daughters, Kate and Sarah (Phoebe) Nicholls, also entered the acting profession. Peg, who studied dancing, stayed at home until 1941

Below left Family games in parlour; framed portrait of George prominently displayed, 1919

Below ' "His Nibs" Sid draws the original design for the famous Rowntree Poster "The Cocoa Nibs" ' when he was 16 years old. It was his first attempt at poster design and was purchased by Messrs Rowntree, 1919

'HisNibs' Sid draws the original design for the famous Rowntree Poster "The Cocoa Nibs"

Above Uncle Sid in the garden,
no date

Above and above right After
Nicholls obtained his first Leica,
he enjoyed making his own
family 'stamp' collection, 1936–7

helping her father with his business and looking after her parents until she married Colonel Bernard Mallinson. Of their three children, James, Margaret and David, the latter is also an actor.

For thirty-four years, between 1905 and 1939, Horace Nicholls prepared each year, with great thought and care, a family album as a Christmas present to his wife. A photographer's family albums are not like a writer's diaries. The pictures are mementoes of happy (and very occasionally sad) times. This is not generally used as an occasion for the photographer to pour out his emotion, but it is often where one can find his most spontaneous, impulsive images.

Many of the pictures in the albums were taken on the beach or during winter holidays abroad and, in the early years, there were plenty of baby pictures. Family games in the parlour, track meets at the children's schools or Uncle Sid jumping in the air are a fair representation of the subjects included. Sometimes the images were witty. The 1909 album ends with a self-portrait of Nicholls holding some string, and where the picture of the string ends, a real piece begins. In the albums for 1936–7 there is a double-page spread of postage stamps, only each one has a tiny family portrait skilfully placed where normally the king or queen would be. Nicholls had a wonderful sense of humour, a great love of life, a deep commitment to photography and a fine sense of balance and proportion. Faith Nicholls, wife of Anthony (Sidney), related a story her husband used to tell:

> One evening, when Tony was about 20, and a rather innocent and unsophisticated 20, he took a girlfriend to the theatre and supper afterwards. Between the theatre and the restaurant he had his wallet pinched and didn't discover this till he went to pay the bill. Being young – the girl was a little older and he had a tremendous crush on her – he was in an agony of embarrassment and asked the girl if she would wait until he saw the Manager. The girl sportingly offered to pay but of course this he could *not* accept. He offered his watch to the Manager until the following day as security, but to his horror the Manager said the dinner was expensive and the watch was not! Crimson with shame he asked to telephone his father and, of course, expected hell, as it was late. To his amazement then (but not at all to his amazement when he told me the story in the security of his forties!) his father roared with laughter, zoomed round in a taxi to the rescue, having first persuaded the Manager to give them both a liqueur with their coffee while they waited! Later he gave Tony a very expensive watch 'in case this sort of thing happens again!'[19]

Horace Walter Nicholls moved to 7 Trent Road, Worthing in 1936. He died of diabetes on 28 July 1941.

Family members, Sandown, Isle of Wight, 1912. The sky has been printed from a separate negative.

1. Undated newspaper clipping in scrapbook compiled by Horace W. Nicholls now in the Collection of the Royal Photographic Society.
2. Brief biographical portrait of Horace W. Nicholls, written by Peg Mallinson. Family collection.
3. Ibid.
4. Collection of the Royal Photographic Society of Great Britain.
5. *The Windsor Chronicle*, December 8, 1899.
6. Catalogue for *A Series of Over 400 First-Class Photographs of Surpassing Interest* by Horace W. Nicholls. Collection of the Royal Photographic Society of Great Britain.
7. *Memorable Incidents and Striking Features of the South African Campaign: A Series of Historic Pictures Printed in Permanent Carbon, from Photographs Taken at the Front*, by Horace W. Nicholls. Collection of the Royal Photographic Society of Great Britain.
8. Family collection.
9. Conversation with Dr Leo De Freitas, authority on popular illustration in the nineteenth century.
10. Ibid.
11. Ibid.
12. Letter dated 7 September 1916 from Horace Walter Nicholls to Mr Nicholson. Imperial War Museum.
13. Letter dated 4 April 1914 from Herbert Ponting. Family Collection.
14. Horace W. Nicholls file. Imperial War Museum.
15. Horace W. Nicholls file. Imperial War Museum.
16. Jane Carmichael 'Home Front 1914–1918: The Photographs of G. P. Lewis and Horace Nicholls, *Creative Camera*, no 247/248 (July/August 1985) 58.
17. Letter dated 3 October 1918 from Horace W. Nicholls to Mr Wallace Roome. Horace W. Nicholls file. Imperial War Museum.
18. Although the photographs Nicholls took were not supposed to be sold to the press, this series was released owing to the public awareness that there was a desperate shortage of munitions and the fact that the pictures powerfully evoked an abundance of supplies.
19. Correspondence dated 22 March 1988 from Faith Nicholls.

TO MY CHILDREN
ALAINA JULIET and KEVIN VICTOR

ACKNOWLEDGMENTS

Without the dedication, support and hard work of Col. Bernard C. Mallinson, H. W. Nicholls' son-in-law, this book would not have been written. His help and goodwill have been invaluable. On my behalf he asked each family member for remembrances and hard facts about Horace Nicholls. Among those I should like to thank are Arthur P. Cox, the family historian and a devoted researcher; Horace W. Nicholls, the photographer's namesake; Violet Hughes, the photographer's only living child; Faith Nicholls, widow of Anthony Nicholls; Dorothy Kirkman, Eric Layton and David Mallinson.

Dr. Leo J. De Freitas guided me through technical points related to early photomechanical reproduction in the popular press. Mrs. E. B. Nagelgast, Curator of the Bensusan Museum of Photography and Library, provided information and prints relating to Nicholls' years in South Africa. Jane Carmichael, Keeper of the Department of Photographs at the Imperial War Museum made important documents available to me.

The Royal Photographic Society has given me full access to all their Nicholls' material. The author would like to thank Mr. Kenneth Warr, Secretary of the Society, for remembering my keen interest in Nicholls since my days as Curator of the Society's collection in the early 1970s and inviting me to write the book. Pam Roberts, Librarian and Brian Coe, Curator of the Royal Photographic Society Collection have, with great geniality, tolerated my lengthy visits, numerous inquiries and calls for help. Hope Kingsley undertook the enormous job of cataloguing the seven thousand glass plate negatives and she and Kate Rouse made excellent prints from them for use in this book. I should also like to thank Amanda Nevill, Centre Administrator, for facilitating my research.

Special thanks to my friends Yorick Blumenfeld, Francesca Kazan and Eileen Willoughby; my husband Barry and my children Alaina and Kevin who, while their mother was investigating the Edwardians at play, could not play with their mother.

All photographs are reproduced courtesy of the Royal Photographic Society of Great Britain, Bath except the following: Family collection: *cover*, 27 (below), 45, 48–9, 51, 55, 69, 70–1, 82–3, 88, 89, 92, 93, 100, 101, 102, 103, 107, 109, 113, 115, 116 (below), 117, 119, 129, 132, 139, 140, 141, 143. The Bensusan Museum of Photography and Library, Johannesburg: 118. The Imperial War Museum, London: 133, 134, 135, 136, 137. Arthur P. Cox: 112

PAVILION BOOKS LIMITED
196 Shaftesbury Avenue, London, WC2H 8JL
in association with Michael Joseph Limited
27 Wrights Lane, Kensington, London W8 5TZ

Designed by Lawrence Edwards

A CIP record for this book is
available from the British Library

ISBN 1 85145 326 1

Typeset by Wyvern Typesetting Limited
Printed and Bound in Italy
by Arnoldo Mondadori

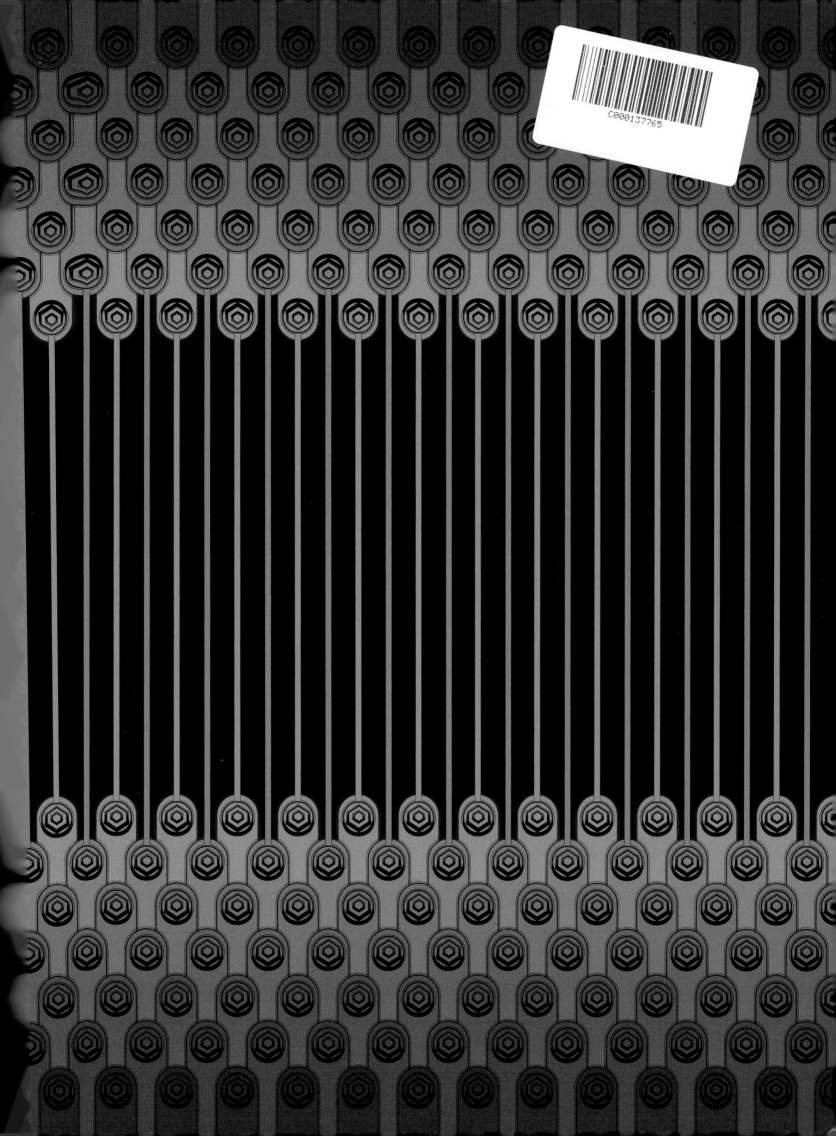

THE COLONY
BY VIKTOR
ANTONOV

The Story of the COLONY
A Structure Celebrating the Triumphs of Technology

Copyright © 2010 by Design Studio Press
All rights reserved.
All illustrations and text in this book are
copyright © owned by Viktor Antonov or their
respective artists unless otherwise noted.
No part of this book may be reproduced or
transmitted in any form or by any means.
electronic or mechanical. including photography. xerography. and videography recording
without written permission from the publisher.
Design Studio Press.

Published by
Design Studio Press
8577 Higuera Street
Culver City. CA 90232

Web site: www.designstudiopress.com
E-mail: info@designstudiopress.com
Printed in China
First edition. July 2010

10 9 8 7 6 5 4 3 2 1

Paperback ISBN 978-1-933492-89-6
Library of Congress Control Number 2010923307

THE STORY OF THE

COLONY

A STRUCTURE CELEBRATING THE TRIUMPHS OF TECHNOLOGY

CREATED & WRITTEN BY

VIKTOR ANTONOV

DESIGN & ILLUSTRATIONS
VIKTOR ANTONOV
CO-WRITING
BENJAMIN MARKUS
CHARACTER DESIGN
MOBY FRANCKE, JOEL
JURION, IVAN GOMEZ
EDITING **KIM ZOLTICH**
TEXT EDITING **TEENA APELES**
BOOK & LOGO DESIGN
TANJA KUMPERMOND
ANNALULU.COM
SPECIAL THANKS TO
ANTHONY HUSO

PREMIERE EDITION

TABLE OF
CONTENTS

PROLOGUE
COLONY

DUNE
DESERT
HEAT
MAN RUNNING

The MAN RAN. FEET SINKING IN THE COOL GREY SAND OF MORNING. HIS MOUTH, A RAGGED HOLE. ALREADY IT WAS GETTING HOT. He gulped air, heavy as molten copper, and stumbled. The desert sent him skittering down the ashen slope. He regained his feet. Behind him, behind the dune, rose a plume of dust and the glint of lances. It was a magnificent horde of mounted archers.

Turbans, skeins of wool, and pointed Mongolian hats sunk their eyes in shadow. The warriors bore shields and arrows. They were wrapped in silk vests, chain mail, marble, and bone. Bloodied animal skins covered their shoulders. Some were half-naked, dark-skinned, each with a shawl around his waist, over which a thick leather belt was strapped, garnishing a large and a small dagger and a silver-mounted pistol. Others wore white cavalry jackets covered with traces of blood from the slain owners. A figure in stunning white followed them; the patterns of his cloak ornate like fallen snow, his dragoon uniform immaculate. The chieftain straddled a massive horse and gazed down at the stumbling, fleeing peasant. In one hand, he held aloft something dark and hooded that moved in the wind. Its shriek echoed off the dunes and drew the horde to a halt. A slow breeze moved down the transient valley, carrying fumes from the horde across the sand.

The clouds of dust caught up with the fleeing man and blew past him in tendrils. He did not look back. He only ran. From the chieftain's arm, the balancing shape launched against the sun, enormous and billowing. It flapped, wings beating audibly in the desert air. Instantly, the hunting eagle crossed over the horde and reached the peasant with effortless grace. The impact could be felt even at a hundred yards: quiet but solid in its connection with the back of the peasant's head. The bird folded on top of the fallen man, pulling a long strip of flesh up from its prey. It paused for a moment, eyes alert, blinking. Human meat hung like a snake in its beak. Beneath its talons, the man's resistance slowly went slack.

The immaculate chieftain smiled and put a golden whistle to his lips. He blew and the bird lifted off the crumpled form. On the signal several horsemen rode forward, dragging a net lined with hooks through the whispering sand...

PART
01

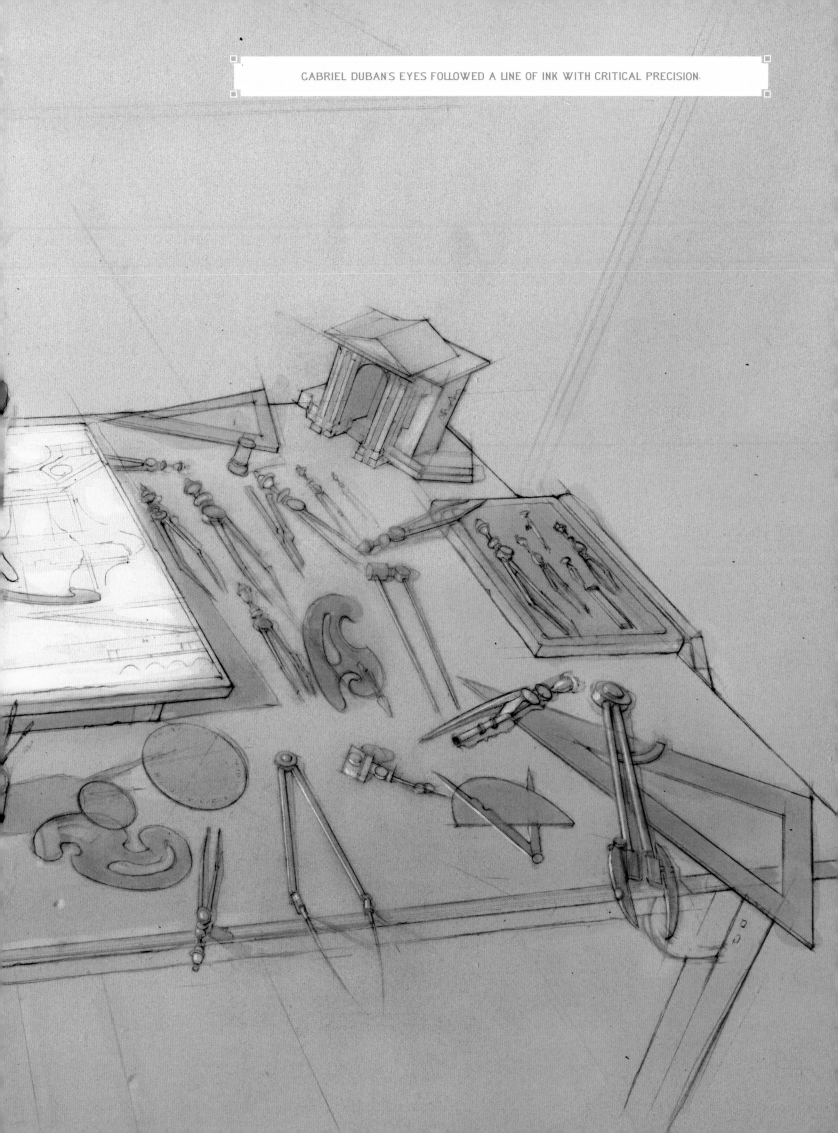

CHAPTER
01

1875
GABRIEL'S OFFICE
FEBRUARY
10TH NOON

GABRIEL DUBAN'S EYES FOLLOWED A LINE OF INK WITH CRITICAL PRECISION AS IT FLOWED SMOOTHLY ALONG A PRISTINE SHEET OF WHITE DRAFTING PAPER. His hands moved with extreme efficiency, quickly marking the blueprint with swift methodical flourishes. He was focused and nearly finished.

"Duban!" Startled, Gabriel jerked his ruler and smeared the line across the page. "Damn it, Jules!" he said, as he turned around to the see his friend, the senior clerk of the Ministry of Colonies, standing in the doorway. Jules winced when he saw the smudge on Gabriel's paper. "Sorry, Gabriel. Girard's waiting." Gabriel's eyes fell back to the smear. Written below were his name, the title junior architectural assistant, and the date February 10, 1875. Gabriel looked at his pocket watch. Twelve forty-five in the afternoon. He pulled himself away from the marred plans and got up to follow Jules to the director's office. "Good luck," said Jules as he reached for the handle. Gabriel smiled painfully.

The heavy doors opened slowly and bright lights streamed in from the wall of windows that leapt up from behind the director's large oak desk. Half blinded, Gabriel held up his arm to stifle the light. A murky silhouette gradually appeared as it shifted against the glaring background. "Good afternoon, Gabriel," said Girard, the Ministry director.

"What can I do for you?" "Good afternoon, Mr. Girard, and thank you for working me into your schedule." Gabriel's eyes were still adjusting to the fierce light, but he could see the director's fingers pressed against the wrinkled skin of his temple as he studied a complex array of documents. The office was full of tables with bas-reliefs, globes, and scale models of cannons. On the walls were ornate maps and colonial trophies such as spears, indigenous masks, and other unidentifiable tools.

Gabriel continued, "Sir, I know you must be aware that I've been at the Ministry for over four years now. I'm meticulous, hardworking, and I think I'm rather good at what I do…" He stopped mid-sentence, as Girard seemed to stiffen. The man had an irregularly shiny forehead, a curled mustache, and a hawk-like nose. Slowly he pointed to a nearby armchair, "Please, have a seat." Gabriel grabbed the red velvet armrest, pulled the chair across the carpet, and sat down, crossing his legs. He seemed ready to continue when Girard cut him off. "So you want a promotion, eh?" Gabriel looked the director in the eye and tightened his jaw. "Sir, you know as well as I that my talent as a draftsman is unmatched here, and you also know my wife recently gave birth. A promotion would not only help us feed our child, it would allow me to move on to much greater projects." "Duban, there are other factors than the work to consider if one is to move to a more responsible position." Gabriel waited patiently for him to continue.

GABRIEL DUBAN

"The clerks who have been promoted always showed some extra commitment to the Ministry, something I haven't exactly seen from you." "But how can I be committed to drafting canalization systems for badly built settlements in Tunisia? I'm no good in my current position! I want to be a part of something significant and I could do twice as much for the colonies if I had more responsibility, and you know it!"

Girard's expression softened. "Duban, I'm not out to get you. I knew your father and I know what you lost in the commune wars, so I'm willing to offer you the position of senior architectural assistant. How does 2,500 francs sound?" Gabriel's jaw dropped slightly. "Very good, sir" "But, there is one condition, of course. You must prove your commitment to the Ministry. As you probably know, there's a very important event coming up." "Yes, the Colonial City of the Future Contest," said Gabriel, nodding his head slowly. "The Minister of Colonies has organized the event and the winning project will be displayed at the 1878 Paris World Fair. The best architects in France will be there! And Europe! All Prix de Rome! Now I know you submitted your project, but for the sake of the Ministry, I would like you to withdraw it and become a member of the jury." "What?" Gabriel blurted out. "This is the real world, Duban. There have always been plenty of fancy ideas, especially with the metal architecture craze. Pretty drawings are fine, but solid attainable ideas are rare. Our job is to select something feasible and, frankly speaking, your work is beyond the reach of any architectural firm in Europe. We're simply not interested in such large-scale endeavors."

Gabriel slouched back in the stiff armchair, deflated, but pensive. "Duban, I've wasted a fair amount of time with you." The director pulled out his watch and wound it. "What'll it be? The jury or the promotion?" "I'm sorry. I can't answer now." Girard sighed. "Fine, you have until the end of the day tomorrow to withdraw, otherwise you forfeit the raise." "Thank you sir," said Gabriel as he stood up to leave.

CHAPTER
01

That evening, he flung on his coat and trudged out of the Palace de la Concorde, turning left onto Rue de Rivoli. He passed the repetitive columns and arches, glancing across the street at the Tuileries gardens and the Louvre. As he walked through Paris, he could envision the buildings as detailed blueprints drawing themselves across the sky. In fact, all of Paris seemed colorless as if he were walking through an unfinished drawing. The limestone facades were a warm gray and the tin rooftops a bit cooler, perfectly matching the sky, as if by design.

He turned left onto Rue Cambon, sinking into himself as the sunlight faded. Lost in his thoughts, he barely noticed the gloomy drizzle tapping him on the shoulders. As he passed Saint-Honoré market, he saw a stooped figure in the corner of his eye. Gabriel buried his face in his scarf and quickened his pace. Beggars were common here. The impact came suddenly, warm and soft. It filled Gabriel's nostrils with old smoke and the bursting sweetness of freshly cut roses. He was so deep in his thoughts it took him a moment to realize he'd plowed into a ragged-looking woman selling flowers. "I beg your pardon!" said Gabriel as he backed away, visibly appalled to have come in contact with the beggar. A dirty scarf covered her face and she had obviously planted herself directly in his path. An enormous collection of strikingly colored rose blossoms exploded in front of her eyes, which was odd for the season. They were a dark burgundy, almost violet, and their sweet smell made him hesitate despite the initial revulsion. "For you, monsieur."

The voice from beneath the scarf was oddly accented. Gabriel thought that maybe she was a Gypsy. He looked at his pocket watch. He was running late again and his wife was at home waiting. He dug in his pocket for some spare change and thrust it at her, reaching for the bouquet. The woman pushed it awkwardly into his hand and the result was painful. He cursed and dropped the flowers, holding his palm up to the light. A curved thorn protruded from his index finger and a trickle of blood ran down his arm. "So sorry," said the woman, who seemed genuinely distraught. She quickly produced a handkerchief from her bulky pockets to clean the wound and Gabriel recoiled in disgust. He attempted to argue, insisting he was fine, but her fingers had already snaked around his wrist and the vice-like hold brought panic to his eyes.

"You have an unusual palm, monsieur," the flower lady hissed. She held Gabriel's hand open before her eyes as she bent back his finger to clean the wound. "I have no more change for a fortune!" Gabriel snapped. He wrenched his hand away and leaned over to grab the roses. "Good evening, madam." The rain started coming down like bullets and he quickly stormed off into the night.

The smell of slate and stew filled the ancient concierge hall of Gabriel's apartment building. He crossed the courtyard and headed for door B. There were no lamps in the yard and he paused, momentarily confused. He had just moved in a week ago with his wife, Marianne, and their four-month-old baby, Daniel, and he'd spent more time at work than at home. After a moment he recognized the blue entrance in the dark and bolted up the five stories, taking two and sometimes three steps at a time.

Bursting into the apartment, he called out to Marianne in a whisper, hiding the roses behind his back. There was no answer. The apartment was crowded with the chattel of the larger accommodations they had recently come from. Gabriel sidled between a bureau and a side table, navigating the space with difficulty. He found Marianne in the living room rocking their sleeping son, Daniel, in her arms. Smiling, she put her finger to her lips. Gabriel grinned and crept forward with exaggerated stealth. He leaned over his wife and kissed her forehead. "He's just fallen asleep," Marianne whispered. "Will you put him in the cradle?" Gabriel took his bundled son and swung him around, gently depositing him on the tiny bed. He looked up and saw a little porcelain virgin dangling from the wall above the crib. "I see you've unpacked your charms," he whispered with a frown. Marianne stuck out her tongue and led him to the kitchen. "How was your day?" she asked as she marveled at the bouquet. "It's too early for roses! You must have paid a fortune. We can't be wasting money..."

Gabriel embraced her suddenly from behind, sending the roses tumbling into the sink and eliciting a shriek. Marianne stifled her laugh and glanced worriedly toward the cradle, but the baby lay fast asleep. "Obviously it must've been good," she said, only with the pretense of scolding him. "It was fine." Gabriel whispered modestly. Instantly she knew he hadn't told her everything. "What are you hiding, Mr. Duban?" "Nothing," said Gabriel, "except that old bastard Girard is finally going to promote me!" Gabriel masked his lie with a devious precision. Marianne's eyes lit up. Her mouth opened wide in a gasp of excitement. She drew his face into her hands and kissed him repeatedly. Between the kisses she spoke, "I told you...I knew you'd get it...I'm so proud of you!" "No more dipping into the savings we inherited from your mother's family," Gabriel promised. "Soon we'll get a bigger place and soon we'll get back everything we've sacrificed." "Is it certain?" she asked. "Yes. I have to act as a juror for Girard at an upcoming competition, but of course it's certain." Marianne clapped her hands and kissed him again. "But, you know," said Gabriel as he continued twisting the lie, "this promotion is not such a big deal. It's just the beginning for us. It will make me much more visible to a circle of very important people...I don't intend on being a clerk my whole life.

I'm good at what I do. I want to start participating! Great things are on the horizon. Huge architectural ventures! We might even be able to go to the colonies! Help make history, Marianne! Think of it. We'd be better off than before the war. It's an architect's world these days, full of technology and designs. Anything is possible!"

Marianne was quiet. She held his hand tenderly and smiled. "Such beautiful dreams in that head of yours, but the promotion is important and I worry a little when you speak of the colonies. People say it's a godless place full of devils." "Marianne, you know I respect god, but the times are changing. Anyway, I refuse to argue about this!" A severe degree of finality accompanied his words. Her lips puckered softly as she held her slender hand to her mouth and yawned. "You're right, let's not argue. It's time for bed." "You go ahead, I'll be a minute."

He watched her walk sleepily down the hall. When she was gone, he crept past the baby and into his study. The walls seemed to growl with printed reproductions of paintings from the Orient. The desk languished under the weight of several stacks of historical books. There was a photo of his father taken in Alexandria; he was wearing a white suit and a tall white helmet. Gabriel lit the lamp and sat down in his chair. Marianne appeared in the doorway. "Are you coming to bed?" "Yes, dear. In a minute." She smiled and vanished. Gabriel took down one of his books, opened it under the yellow light of the oil lamp, and began to read.

CHAPTER 02

1875
MINISTRY COLONIES
FUTURE CONTEST
12TH FEB

GABRIEL SLOWLY WEAVED THROUGH THE CROWD OF COATTAILS AND COMPETITORS WHO HAD GATHERED IN THE GRAND HALL OF THE MINISTRY OF COLONIES TO PARTICIPATE IN THE COLONIAL CITY OF THE FUTURE CONTEST. To his right was a row of tables on wheels bearing the weight of white model cities of varying size and detail. Eventually he came to a great doorway, which led to the jury room. A velvet stage curtain had been rigged to hide it from view. He lifted the corner and peered inside.

The walls of the room were as red as an abattoir, traced with subtle symbolic patterns and hung with large paintings that represented the French Republic as a winged, voluptuous, bare-breasted woman who interacted with various African and Arab tribes. Three long tables had been placed in a U-shape and covered with green fabric. At the center of the room, the displays would be shown one at a time. There he saw Girard mingling among the sideburns, waistcoats, and wide ascot ties.

"Gentlemen!" Girard pitched his voice above the tumult, "please take your seats. We're ready to begin." Gabriel shuffled back between the competing architects and took his place in a lavish armchair behind his model. Unlike the others, Gabriel had covered his miniature city with a large white sheet. He watched as the first project rolled in, pushed by valets and accompanied by a nondescript gentleman who introduced himself as the architect responsible for an accurate model of a colonial town with an intricate irrigation and canalization system. As the architect's muffled voice trailed off behind the curtain, Gabriel noticed another set of valets bringing in a set of orthographic drawings of water towers, locks, and escapes. He felt himself drift. He hadn't slept much.

The next project featured an urban plan favoring commerce with a Roman-style forum or market at its center. The ability to accommodate a steady influx of goods and transportation seemed to be the main advantage of the design.

Finally Gabriel heard his name called. The valets approached his table and attempted to remove the white sheet as they wheeled his model into the jury room, but Gabriel grabbed one of their arms and indicated that he'd like to keep it covered. While attempting to fix his tie and push back his hair, Gabriel's eyes met Girard's. Gabriel faced the jury with confidence, letting Girard's words pass through him like water in a sieve. He waited until the judges quieted and gently pulled the sheet from his model. Some of the judges gasped and others sneered. Underneath stood a miniature of astonishing design and fragility. It appeared to be a town or a city on a platform, suspended by a network of cables from four pillars whose scale suggested they would be enormous if they were actually built. The structure was utterly fantastic. The suspension lines crisscrossed neatly, forming lovely geometric patterns, and like an undiscovered insect from the jungles of Africa, the hanging city seemed to stare back at the jury from between its powerfully pillared legs. Gabriel turned to the valets and motioned for them to set up his drawings on easels around the room that mostly depicted ink washes of aristocratic couples strolling on hanging alleys and byways. Behind the subtle pastel colors of the buildings, he'd painted the sky an inviting tropical blue. The room was quiet for a moment and Gabriel looked around at the circle of faces. Some wore smirks. Girard seemed particularly ill-humored.

"Gentleman, I am grateful for the opportunity to present a project I've been developing for many years now," said Gabriel. "What you see is a settlement town, suspended on steel cables. It's a prefabricated design that could be assembled over any new colonial territory in a matter of months. All the pieces could be manufactured here, in Paris, and then shipped to the colony by rail. It will be a sight of dramatic monumentality that will symbolize the power of the colonizing nation as well as a chance for France to reestablish itself as a great industrial and civilizing power in the aftermath of our unfortunate war with Prussia." Gabriel went on to describe in detail the town's fortification system; how it would be safe from hostile natives while its many luxurious balconies still provided breathtaking views of the land below.

"Terraces and gardens will allow residents to survey the colony like the gods on Olympus!" Several of the jury members seemed slightly interested while others nodded off and snapped back into reality as if nothing had happened. Girard stared at Gabriel as if his idea was utterly preposterous. Gabriel paused to take a sip of water before he continued. "Now, about the cables. Steel is ideal. Only steel cables are capable of supporting a city over 240 meters in the air. Only steel has the strength and flexibility to resist the winds that would undoubtedly buffet such a construction." Gabriel gulped down the last of his water and added, "Also a fifth pillar, although not needed, would guarantee the structure's overall strength, which if you're willing to do the math, should satisfy every skeptic in this room." Hastily he thanked the judges and quickly wheeled his presentation back through the curtain with a sigh of relief. Back in the hallway he paid no more attention to any of the projects and let himself doze off in his hefty armchair. Suddenly he was on a long terrace of his suspended city, running after a woman in an elegant dress and fluttering scarf. He dodged under metal buttresses and zigzagged between convoluted networks of steel cables. His feet seemed to float effortlessly beneath him. In the distance he saw her stop at a railing to take in the view when a large gust of wind sent her scarf billowing toward him like a ballerina dancing to the symphony of wind. Laughing, he pulled the fabric from his eyes only to see the vast expanse of desert stretching out before him. One of the anchorages holding up the city from his drawings loomed above him as he reached the end of the platform. Gasping in excitement he grabbed at the woman's arm, but the loud sound of clapping blurred out her face, like blotchy watercolors.

Gabriel awoke to find the parade of projects coming to an end. All of the architects were standing up and Gabriel rose to his feet as well. Girard and the rest of the jury were standing in the hall getting ready for the final ceremony. Girard stepped forward holding a trophy as he made the final announcement. "My dear competitors, the jury has chosen a winner for the 1875 Colonial City of the Future Contest. We are proud to present the grand prize to Jacques Dubert for his intricately designed Roman-style town featuring a complex irrigation and canalization system." Applause filled the air yet again and the participating architects surrounded him with congratulations. Gabriel looked sick and turned away.

As the judges began to leave, he overheard one of them making a joke about his project. "Good God! It's so absurd! A hanging city? There's no place on earth such a thing could be built! It's utterly ridiculous..." The joke drew another critic's attention. "With all due respect, sir, not only is that structure feasible, but it's certainly the most innovative design

we saw today." Several heads turned in his direction, including the hawk-nosed skull of Girard, but after catching Girard's eye, the critic chuckled uncomfortably and continued speaking softly to his companion as if nothing had happened.

A tall architect with a thick red mustache and Nordic cheekbones stood up in Gabriel's defense. "Gentlemen!" he said, as Gabriel realized he'd never seen him before, "Duban's structure is realistic! It can be made to work and if you want to award the grand prize to another conventional city then you're making a mistake!" The winning architect flashed him an insulted look and Gabriel found himself smiling at the defense. Several of the critics laughed aloud at his outburst. "No one is going to invest in such a risky enterprise, Mr. uh..." The nearest judge searched for the stranger's name on a card. "Yes, who are you?" asked Girard, bristling with irritation. The room had become quiet and all eyes were on the architect who stood up for Gabriel. "Who I am is of no significance. The genius of Mr. Duban's design is unmatched here and you're a fool if you can't see it." Girard was fuming as he slowly turned to the other judges. "Gentlemen! Of course Mr. Duban's project is absurd! I thought we all agreed on that." He looked directly at Gabriel. "Steel or not, it could never stand, even in a country with no wind. Imagine the excavation work needed just for one of the pillars! There are no machines capable of moving such a large quantity of earth!"

Suddenly a shrill voice reached out from the other side of the hall, a senior jury member dropping his opinion into the silence. "Mr. Girard, clearly not all of us agree. Duban could be right. The design has potential if the suspension is calculated correctly." Girard looked at the other judge angrily. "The choice has been made and the contest is over! What is the jury asking for? A recount?" Girard's eyes scanned the crowd menacingly, but no one spoke. The debate was over and the valets began helping the judges clear their tables. Girard gave Gabriel a final triumphant look and he strode from the building with the rest of the judges at his heels.

The room quickly emptied and the lights seemed to dim. Gabriel began wheeling out his model and rushed down the long hallway. As he walked backward, he bumped into a woman carrying a tray with documents in long tubes. The tray flipped and sent the tubes rolling all over the floor.

"I beg your pardon, excuse my clumsiness, madam," he said, dropping to the floor to start picking them up. The woman went down on her knees, too, next to him. Their foreheads almost touched when he looked at her for the first time—she was young, Mediterranean or Oriental, with a headband and an exquisite black butterfly veil partially covering her carefully made-up face. "Don't worry, it's nothing," she said with a light accent, and laughed. She got up and looked down at him, smiling. She wore a low-cut dress with a flower in her bosom. Her eyes were large and liquid. Dark, thick eyebrows arched above them. Gabriel straightened up, faced her, and nodded. He tried to move ahead but she took a little step and stood in front of him. Behind her a striking man dressed in a white military uniform with gold epaulettes and tall black boots stepped out of the shadows. He had a powerful demeanor, but his gentle expression suggested soft charisma. Judging by the ornaments on his uniform he was Russian. The man signaled behind him and a group of what looked like high-ranking officials appeared out of nowhere. The soldiers raised their sabers and brought them to their stern faces in a quick salute as they took their place behind Gabriel. The Oriental woman stepped toward Gabriel and introduced herself. "Hello, Mr. Duban. I have the privilege to introduce you to Grand Duke Konstantin Orlof, who's here to meet you personally. I'm his majesty's assistant, my name is Senna, spelled with a double 'n.'" She spoke with a light accent and he felt there was something familiar about her. The voice was deep and smoky and Gabriel felt it in his plexus. She pushed a sleek strand of jet-black hair behind one ear, revealing a glistening teardrop earring. "We've been following your work for quite some time, Mr. Duban." She held out her hand and laughed sweetly when Gabriel politely kissed it.

"Mr. Duban, we're very interested in your newest design and would be honored if you would attend a celebration tomorrow night where we might discuss an architectural contract. We have a proposition for you." She handed him a small envelope with a red seal. "Simply give them this and tell them my name. I'll be waiting for you inside." Gabriel followed them to the front of the building and the doors slammed open. He watched as the last two uniformed men marched down the building steps taking their place in two geometrically precise lines that ran down the sides of the building's wide staircase.

"Who are these people?" thought Gabriel. Somehow the dark Oriental look of the guards told him they were from somewhere further east than Russia. As the man in white approached the black carriage, a valet stepped swiftly behind him and covered his shoulders with a voluminous silver mantle. After he had climbed into the coach and sat down, another valet stepped up and covered his legs to the knee with an extravagant fur-trimmed velvet cloak. After methodically wrapping it around his feet, he performed a long low bow and took his place at the front of the carriage. The man sat erect and expressionless in the upholstered cabin as he allowed himself to be manipulated like an infant. Everyone bowed and stayed with their heads down until the driver whipped the horse into action. As the coach gained speed, the man in white gracefully turned his head until his eyes met Gabriel's. They were sensual, sapphire eyes. Gabriel realized he must've only been in his forties, but his beautiful dark face showed a much deeper wisdom. The horses trotted away, but the rest of the procession remained. Gabriel's eyes followed the carriage dreamily as it rolled off down the street.

CHAPTER
02

THE MAN ALLOWED HIMSELF TO BE MANIPULATED LIKE AN INFANT.

CHAPTER 03

EVENING CAFEBAR SMOKEY 03 MURKY

THE ABSINTHE HOUR ON THE BOULEVARDS BEGAN AT ABOUT HALF-PAST FIVE AND LASTED UNTIL ABOUT HALF-PAST SEVEN. BUT NEVER ENDED IN CAFE DE LA NOUVELLE ATHENES. A PARTITION. RISING A FEW FEET OVER THE PATRONS' HEADS. SEPARATED THE GLASS FRONT FROM THE MAIN AREA OF THE CAFE.

The place was already smoky although there were only a few customers at the counter. Inside, large mirrors reflected each other and created a maze of endless, crooked corridors. At the corner booth Gabriel sat listlessly blowing smoke rings and stirring the opal green liquid in his glass when Jules spoke to him in a low voice.

"So, Jacob's coming too? Let's get through this fast then. You know how I feel about the man. What did you want to discuss?" Gabriel looked up at his friend with somewhat glassy eyes and brought him closer. "Listen, Jules! Something happened to me after the contest that I know you're not going to believe, so just hear me out, okay?" Jules uncomfortably pushed him away. "I already know what happened. I got the news straight from Girard." He looked around the murky bar. "Why the hell do we have to meet in a place like this? Have you gotten involved in the arts and poetry, or just developed a drinking habit?" "Maybe both," said Gabriel as he sucked back half his glass. "So tell me, what'd Girard say about the contest?" "Just that you're fired!" Jules's acrid tone brought Gabriel up with a start, but he quickly gathered himself together. "Well, there's something he didn't tell you." "What the hell are you talking about?" Gabriel sighed and he spoke to Jules in a hushed voice. "Just listen to me, okay! After the contest this strange army of Oriental-looking guards stormed into the hallway with some Russian duke! So I followed them out front and his assistant told me that this general guy is actually interested in building my city!" "And look," Gabriel rummaged in his jacket until he found Senna's invitation, "they've invited me to a celebration and will propose me a deal tomorrow night." Jules's expression went unchanged. "Good Lord, how much absinthe have you drank?" "Come on, Jules, have I ever lied to you?" "That's not the question! The question is when are you going to give up these dreams of avant-garde architecture? No one is going to build your city and that's a fact!"

The waiter picked up Jules's glass and inquired if the gentlemen would care for another. For a moment Gabriel had no words, then, gulping down the rest of his drink, he answered in a hoarse voice, "Yes, please." He looked back at Jules. "You've really changed since our school years. You used to think differently! Remember our heroes, the fathers of metal architecture in France, Henri Labrouste, Victor Baltard. The best were always laughed at. Everybody thought Les Halles was an impossible venture at first, and I know my city sounds like a myth, but it's exactly the kind of thing that could make the history books. Is it so hard to believe that it could finally happen?" "It's not so easy to believe lies!" Jules said vindictively. "And what if it's the truth?" came a nearby voice. The two men swiveled around in their seats. "Ah, shit!" Jules swore when he saw Jacob standing in front of them.

He was a tall, slender man with tanned skin, close-set eyes, and a thin mustache. Without asking, he smoothly slid into the booth next to Jules. "Gentlemen, riends, what a joy to find you here, especially you, Jules! It seems you've changed social circles since you got involved in Ministry matters." "I've been busy. In fact, I'll be leaving any minute now," Jules replied, looking away. Jacob snapped his fingers to get the waiter's attention, then smiled and tapped the table with his newspaper. "Just a carafe of water, please."

After the waiter brought it and left, Jacob whispered, "Drinks are on me, just pretend you see nothing." He unscrewed the ivory dog-head handle of his cane and with a swift gesture poured something out of the tube into their glasses. Jules rolled his eyes, but a tired smile appeared on Gabriel's face. "Perhaps you'd like to take a look at today's paper before you go, Jules?" asked Jacob as he tossed the roll in front of him. Jacob read out loud: "The rebellious town of Kokand was recently conquered by the czar's general Skobelev. It will be a fortified city that will become the new capital Asia Minor and the most important trading post on the mythical Silk Road. The settlement will be the key to the economical renaissance and stability of the region. Trade taxes from merchants in Europe, Asia, and the Middle East will allow the settlement to flourish as a profitable enterprise." "You see, it states here that a Russian viceroy by the name of Orlof has come to Paris to choose the architect who will design the layout for the empire's new colony. The actual blueprints haven't yet been revealed." "Well, that architect is me!"

Gabriel's eyes began to sparkle and before Jacob could say another word, he'd snatched the paper from Jules and pulled out a small magnifying glass from his pocket. Quickly he compared the name on the paper with the one written on the red seal of Senna's invitation. "Viceroy Orlof!" Gabriel exclaimed as he found the tiny name on the seal. "The same spelling!" He shoved the paper and the envelope back across the table and leaned back, staring at Jules with a grin. "Oh, no," said Jules, "forget about it!" "It's a shame," said Gabriel. "What's a shame?" asked Jules. "It's a shame that the Russian empire is more open to progress than France, the cradle of culture. I told you nothing's changing here! Everything's established and stale!" Gabriel released a long puff of smoke that lingered under the low-watt lamp hanging over the table. "Gabriel," said Jules, "listen to me carefully! Your suspended city would be difficult to build even in the best of locations...but Turkistan! I guess you haven't heard, but that place is a miserable wasteland, full of various tribes who've been fighting for centuries. No country has been able to colonize it and nothing will get built there. Turkistan is the worst place God created and so he abandoned it!"

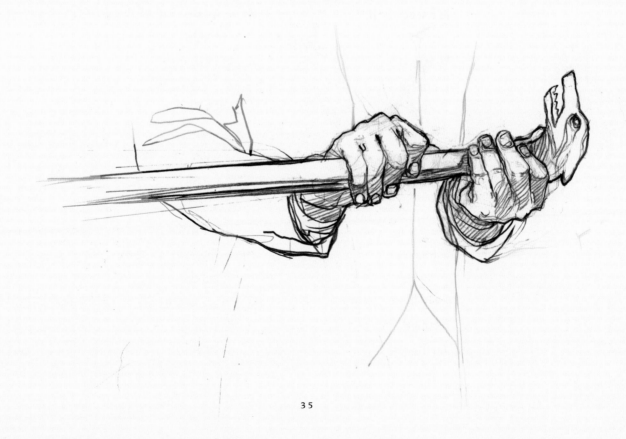

Gabriel tapped the table. "New, innovative cities can only be built in the colonies! No one believed in the Suez Canal either. Or what about the Russian capital St. Petersburg? It was built on a swamp for Christ's sake!" "You know, Gabriel, I'll have to agree with Jules on this one," interjected Jacob. "I spent some years in Africa, you know, with the ivory trade and all," he said, pulling up his sleeve revealing an ugly scar on his hairless forearm, "and one can really get stung there. The natives only understand one language, the language of violence. Of course, fortunes can be made and the women are easy, nonetheless...the locals can't be trusted..." "Technology is the best way to enlighten the tribes," Gabriel countered. "I'm sure that Viceroy Orlof's company will civilize the area." "You've gone mad!" Jules burst out.

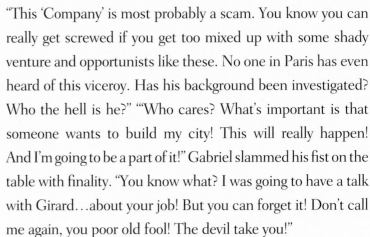

"This 'Company' is most probably a scam. You know you can really get screwed if you get too mixed up with some shady venture and opportunists like these. No one in Paris has even heard of this viceroy. Has his background been investigated? Who the hell is he?" "Who cares? What's important is that someone wants to build my city! This will really happen! And I'm going to be a part of it!" Gabriel slammed his fist on the table with finality. "You know what? I was going to have a talk with Girard...about your job! But you can forget it! Don't call me again, you poor old fool! The devil take you!"

The waiter pretended to polish a brass railing behind them and tilted his head trying to hear something exciting. Gabriel's eyes were shining, his cheeks were glowing, and nothing could spoil his joy. "That's fine, go back to your master. I've had enough of your stinking Ministry anyhow!" Jules threw some change on the table and stormed out. Jacob lifted his glass, "Bravo! You were magnificent, my friend! I'll drink to this."

At nine-thirty the next evening Gabriel was standing at the address listed on Senna's invitation. He was dressed in his finest gray jacket, crisp waistcoat, and elegant tasseled shoes. He'd told Marianne he would be dining with his coworkers to celebrate his promotion and wasn't sure when he'd be home. "Good evening, monsieur," said one of the doormen. "May we be of any assistance?" said the exact same voice from behind him.

36

CHAPTER
03

Gabriel jumped when he turned around and noticed he was standing in the midst of two look-alikes. They were both thick-necked bald men wearing the exact same button-up coats and white gloves. As they moved next to one another the lamps behind their heads formed halos in the smoky air.

"Yes, I'm here for the party," Gabriel said uneasily. "Here's my invitation." He took the piece of paper out of the envelope and handed it to one of them. The man examined the paper. "The party, monsieur?" he said questioningly as he turned it around in careful examination. Finally he passed it on to the second doorman who flipped it against the light as if looking for a watermark. "May I ask where you acquired this, 'invitation'?" "Yes, a lady gave it to me yesterday right after the Colonial City of the Future Contest at the Ministry of Colonies." Both twins smiled slightly and looked at each other. "A lady, monsieur? Do you happen to recall her name?" "Her name?" repeated Gabriel. "Yes, of the lady who gave you the invitation." "Yes, a dark-haired lady..." he hesitated. "Miss Senna invited me. I believe she's Viceroy Orlof's assistant." A brief silence followed and one of them finally said, "Would you be so kind as to wait here, I'll be back shortly." He turned and the door whispered shut behind him. The other doorman remained at his post, silently staring at Gabriel with a polite smile. Time passed and soon it began to drizzle. Gabriel paced back and forth on the stairs trying to make out the muffled sounds that occasionally drifted through an open window above him.

Time passed slowly and Gabriel was beginning to get wet and irritated. Eventually he stopped in front of the second twin giving him a steady look of contained vexation while raindrops ran down his face, but the stalwart guard continued to eye him without faze. After what seemed like an eternity, the first man returned, keeping the door open and pronounced, with no undue ceremony, "Welcome to the Compagnie Universelle, Monsieur Duban. Please enjoy your evening."

Gabriel passed the inscrutable twins, walked up another staircase, and followed a winding path of tall candles that led to a double door manned by two more rather burly servants. When they saw him they bowed and simultaneously opened the door. As Gabriel stepped inside, the buzz of light and a mixture of exotic scents exploded in his face. The sounds of laughter and drunkenness rose over the low murmur of conversation and he quickly noticed that it was an Oriental-themed party decorated with unusual plants whose labyrinthine foliage gave off a strange luster. The hall's towering colonnades were entwined with enormous roses heavy with scent and there was an empty stage in the back where thick tapestries hung in the shadows. Fountains of champagne made foaming jets and dark-skinned men with red headbands were filling shallow goblets and passing them to guests.

FOUNTAINS OF CHAMPAGNE MADE FOAMING JETS AND DARK SKINNED MEN WERE FILLING GOBLETS AND PASSING THEM TO GUESTS.

Incense smoldered on tall, ornately wrought candleholders and women with veiled faces carried silver trays piled high with delicate pastries and sparkling bowls of spiced nuts and candied fruit. There were fancy, elegant couples, trendy bourgeois youth, and a few modest Parisians trying to blend in. Groups of well-fed elderly men with blushed cheeks and open collars smoked water pipes while playing dice on low tables and reclining on the plushest of carpets and embroidered cushions. Gabriel looked a bit lost as he tried to take in the colorful scene, hoping to find Senna, the viceroy, or any other familiar face among the mixed crowd. As he advanced to the center of the party he noticed a group of men dressed like Nubian, Anatolian , and Ethiopian slave guards carefully observing the event. Gabriel had to push his way through the dense clusters of guests and an elderly couple raised their monocles in tandem to inspect him. Twice he saw silhouettes looking like Senna's, but as he got closer they all turned out to be strangers. He was almost sure he recognized a couple of fashionable Parisian writers, a notary, and even a minister in the crowd. Finally, he thought he spotted the chief waiter from La Nouvelle-Athènes dressed in a striped smoking jacket, which seemed odd, but he felt like talking to somebody so he approached him.

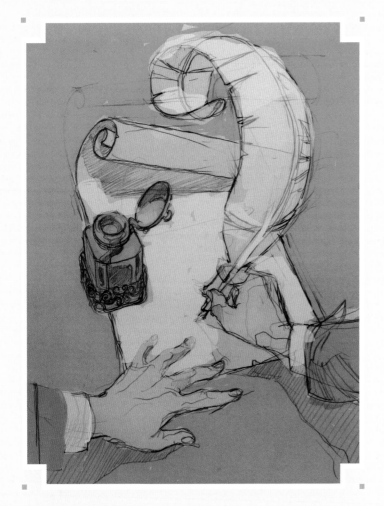

"Baptist, is that you? How did you end up here?" The man frowned slightly, shook his head energetically and answered something in Russian when a gong rang throughout the hall and the lights dimmed. Everyone turned their attention forward. A bald man in a scarlet robe and upturned slippers walked onstage with his arms outstretched. He held a flat drum between his thumb and palm and began to play: first a light rapid tapping sound with nimble fingers, then alternating thumps with his open hand as he advanced with tiny steps. The little silver tassels on his slippers trembled and the crowd grew quieter as the drumbeats drowned out the surrounding conversations.

Three female dancers in shimmering blue and yellow dresses followed the drummer; each one with hair in four long braids reaching to their knees. As the drumbeat changed, the dancers spread their slender arms and moved like a wave to the rhythm of the drum. Eventually they began spinning in a dizzying rotation while effortlessly dipping their bodies backward. The blur of their golden dresses burned on stage like the glowing tail of a phoenix, and the dancers continued to bend backwards until their bodies formed perfect arches and their foreheads almost touched the floor. The fiery birds had transformed into supple serpents. Slowly they rose again to perform a short pantomime to a calmer rhythm, but when the beat suddenly picked up, their bodies twirled into ever-widening circles, and their heads followed half a turn later. Only when their skirts and braids rose up spinning parallel to the floor in a flurry of black whips, did they begin to slow. Finally the dancers came to a standstill. The three of them bowed low and ran from the stage. Applause and exuberant cheers spread throughout the room.

Another gong sounded and the room grew silent. After a second and third gong finished reverberating from one end of the hall to the next, the master of ceremonies appeared and the crowd looked on with an energetic anticipation as they awaited the next announcement. "Ladies and gentlemen, your attention, please! We've arrived at the climax of this truly beautiful evening. We're here to celebrate the creation of our new architectural venture and we would like to invite a select few from the lucky group that you represent for a rare opportunity in financing our project. I'm glad to see that the attendance tonight is excellent and you, the privileged people standing before me, will be the first to hear our call for public subscription and investment in our company. So without further ado, let us welcome our founder, the grand duke of Russia and newly appointed viceroy of Kokand, Konstantin Orlof. As well as one of the most daring architects of our century, Mr. Gabriel Duban." The master of ceremonies held out his hand inviting Gabriel on stage.

Gabriel looked around. He was surprised. The last thing he'd been expecting was to be invited onstage. Two of the viceroy's officials approached him from behind and led him up a small set of stairs to the left of the stage. Gradually Gabriel took a deep breath as he advanced to his place alongside Orlof, who was wearing an immaculate variation of his uniform from the previous night. Without turning his head, the viceroy gave him a reassuring glance with just enough of a smile to pass on the same charismatic disposition Gabriel had noticed the night before. When he'd relaxed, the master of ceremonies continued:

"The Universal Company of Colonial Construction, founded in 1875 with a share capital of two hundred million francs, represents, in the immediate future, a considerable capital gain. In execution of the decision made on the February 15, 1875, by the General Assembly of Shareholders, a public subscription for the investment of 333,333 shares created by the Universal Company of Colonial Construction is opened under the following terms:

These shares are in bond form and listed on the Paris Stock Exchange. They are sold for 300 francs a piece, which is payable on October 1, 1875. They shall accrue an annual interest of 300 francs, payable by a half-year period.

On April 1 and October 1 of each year, without duty or deduction, they shall be redeemable at 500 francs over 50 years by quarterly draw. The first draw shall take place on September 15, 1875, and the redemption of the issued shares shall be effective on the following October 1 of each year, without duty or deduction, they shall be redeemable at 500 francs over 50 years by quarterly draw. The first draw shall take place on September 15, 1875, and the redemption of the issued shares shall be effective on the following October 1, and so on for every three months.

The subscription shall be open from Monday the 26th of April.

Subscription may not be conducted by correspondence.

Applause shook the entire building and Gabriel's heart began beating faste A large glowing smile appeared on the viceroy's face as they walked behind the nearest curtain. Backstage was a mess of colorful tapestries, acrobats, dancers, and performers of all types. Gabriel felt a scented hand slide under his arm and he looked over to see Senna walking beside him in a radiant black silk dress with cutout sleeves and jeweled accents. With a warm smile she turned toward Gabriel, "So are you interested or not?" "In what?" "In selling your design to the company?" Speechless, Gabriel nodded his head in approval. "All you have to do is sign the following contract." A couple of Orlof's officials rolled out a sheet of paper for Gabriel as the viceroy stood by waiting.

Too excited and dizzy to focus well, he hastily read trough the papers, over and over. He believed he understood the general conditions of the contract; some parts were foggy, but did he have another chance? One should jump on such opportunities, or they disappear like mirages. On the fourth read the letters seemed to move and spin into hieroglyphs, and Gabriel just signed. Everybody applauded. As soon as Gabriel's pen left the paper, the viceroy seemed to have mysteriously vanished into the air. He turned to Senna and noticed her eyes were unusually shiny underneath her butterfly veil and her bare shoulders moved up and down as fast as she'd been running. Gabriel had many questions for her. "Well, you invited me, now can you please tell me everything about…" Before he could finish, the grand band picked up Josef Strauss's "Delirien Waltz" and they were encircled by tens of couples. Senna finished Gabriel's champagne, took his hanand they began to dance, twirling among the colors of the Parisian upper class.

CHAPTER
03

Gabriel quickly lost all notion of time or how long he'd been at the party. As Senna danced closer to him, her breasts pressed softly against his chest and her hands began burning in his. As she snuggled even closer, Gabriel could almost feel the scent of jasmine and musk and his head started wheeling. He felt a vague guilt and tried hard to remember something, but he didn't know what. He pulled back from her; their eyes held each other's for a moment and then he mumbled, "Thank you for everything, but I'm afraid I've had a bit too much…I must leave at once. Good night!" He rushed to the door, but before he made it halfway across the hall, Senna called after him. "Meet me here on Monday at eight o'clock. The Ministry doesn't even know what they are missing." Outside he was glad to feel the cold air hit his face.

CHAPTER 04

NIGHT WITH GABRIEL'S HOME MARIANNE

GABRIEL GOT HOME. SHUT THE DOOR QUIETLY. AND PASSED INTO THE SALON. MARIANNE WAS IN THE ARMCHAIR WITH HER EYES CLOSED AND THE FLAME OF A SHORT CANDLE STUB GUTTERED ON THE TABLE. BACKLIGHTING HER HAIR. She had fallen asleep while waiting for him.

Slipping around the edge of the sofa, he caught the flutter of her eyelids. Marianne raised her head, smiled, and reached for him, but as soon as she fully opened her eyes the smile faded. She rubbed her forehead with the tips of her fingers as if she had a headache. "You know I don't like being alone with Daniel at night. Where have you been all this time?" "You won't believe it! I had the most incredible evening!" He went over and knelt at her feet, taking her hand and kissing it. "What is that smell on you?" "It's incense from the East. Listen, I have to tell you something!" "You mean about your dinner?" He frowned, "The dinner? I mean, after the dinner. Just listen, Marianne, fortune has finally smiled on us! The duke of Russia, Viceroy Orlof, wants to build my city?" "Where?" "In the province/colony of Kokand in Turkistan. I have a meeting with him tomorrow." "Turkistan? We need to go to bed, dear," interrupted Marianne with a yawn as she got up, pulling her shawl tightly around her shoulders and picking up the candle.

"What do you mean? This is the best thing that's happened to us in years and you want to sleep! We should open a bottle of champagne!" Before she could leave, Gabriel pulled out his copy of the viceroy's check to show her. "My Lord!" said Marianne, as her eyes grew bigger.

A muffled whine came from the baby's room and she put her finger to his lips. Then she took him by the hand and led him into the bedroom. "Gabriel, what did you do?" She looked at him suspiciously. "I told you, Viceroy Orlof has bought my design for the hanging city and he wants to hire me as the chief architect!" "But what does that mean? What about the Ministry? Gabriel, I'm not moving Daniel to those colonies!" Marianne seemed frightened, even horrified at the news. "Go back to wherever you got the check and return it. I want a normal husband with a normal job!" "This is more than a normal job, it's the chance of a lifetime. I'm gonna quit the Ministry and work for the viceroy." "Quit the Ministry!" she exclaimed. "But next month people all over Paris are going to be investing thousands, possibly millions of francs into this city and we'll be stinking rich! Don't you understand? I don't need that job. This is the real thing! I got paid for a beautiful design I spent half my life working on. So be happy! Spend the money!" "The last thing I want is anything to do with the colonies. Take the money back. I don't want it and we don't need it." "So we compromise. I'll deal with the viceroy and the negotiations concerning the city and I'll keep my job." "Fine," said Marianne as she retreated to her side of the bed and crawled under the covers. Gabriel pulled off his jacket and got ready for bed.

The next day, Gabriel met Jacob for lunch at la Nouvelle-Athènes. It was around one-thirty in the afternoon and Pigalle was bustling with traffic in the afternoon. When he entered the bar his eyes had to adjust to the darkness before he spotted Jacob in the corner languidly blowing smoke rings and finishing a coffee. Jacob looked up at him and forced a tired grin, "Yeah, well you've no idea what I've been doing to myself these days." A short, thick-nosed waiter approached them and stood silently by their table. "Champagne," said Gabriel as he slid a couple banknotes into his vest, "the best in the house, please." He turned back to Jacob who looked at him incredulously. "Since when do you have money for champagne?" "Now it's my turn to celebrate." Jacob waited for him to continue.

"I've done it, they're finally going to build it!" "Your city?" "Yes! My city!" Gabriel tried to look modest. "Listen, the real reason why I wanted us to meet is to let you in on the venture. At 8 o'clock in the morning on Monday the 26th of April the subscription will be open and those shares are going to be worth a fortune, Jacob. You have to invest in this thing. It's an opportunity I don't want you to miss and the sooner we raise the funds the better." He listened intently and slowly nodded. "And you're sure about this?" "Of course, I'm sure. It's my project. Come the the whole city will be throwing money into it. Anyway, you're not the only one. Investors will be flocking and there will be no stocks left soon."Jacob laughed. "I don't know, let me think about it. You know I owe money all over town, just got a brand new loan to repay my previous gambling debts. See, I'm over if I screw up once more." "I'm offering you chance to come back on the top of things here," said Gabriel. "A chance of a lifetime. Just one more thing, don't tell anyone I lost my job. I lied to Marianne."

ONLY STEEL CABLES ARE CAPABLE OF SUPPORTING A CITY OVER TWO HUNDRED FORTY METERS IN THE AIR.

CHAPTER 05

MORNING
WORKPLACE
COMPAGNIE UNIVERSALE
8 O'CLOCK

GABRIEL STARTED WORK AT THE NEW OFFICE AND EVERYTHING WENT OFF WITHOUT A HITCH. ORIGINALLY HE'D BEEN SLEEPING IN TO AVOID TALKING ABOUT WORK WITH MARIANNE. BUT SHE WOULD STILL PRESS HIM WITH QUESTIONS. SO HE STARTED A NEW ROUTINE. He would get up early, have a perfect shave, and leave the apartment precisely at 8 o'clock. At a quarter past, he would arrive at his new workplace, La Compagnie Universelle on Rue de la Chaussée-d'Antin and sprint up the beautiful marble staircase. His new office was on the top floor and the viceroy had spared no expense on his private workspace, which was equipped with every amenity imaginable. At approximately eight-thirty an assistant would enter and inform him on the details of the city's construction. Then Gabriel received a detailed list of areas that needed his attention, mostly recalculations and designs that were required in order to proceed with the next steps of the building process.

When Gabriel finished reviewing the designs of the company draftsmen, he was done for the day. Usually he finished around noon and he would take his drawing kit and wander the city to sit in cafés and reflect on the world. Sometimes he'd even cross the river and go to the Luxembourg Gardens to sit beneath the shade of the trees and draw for hours.

CHAPTER
05

He was living through the rhythm of his journal and for the first time in his life he felt truly proud of his work. In the late afternoon he always spent endless hours meticulously sketching and drafting in his notebook, determined to make the city indestructible by refining an added safety suspension system.

The results were hundreds of little blackened pages full of drawings and numbers that he'd carefully transcribed and shipped to the viceroy's office in Turkistan. He noticed from the company journal that the second issue had printed a picture of the impressive local headquarters. They were set in an ancient stone complex, a temple-like building with large arches.

The viceroy was quoted: *"In the name of the Compagnie Universelle de Construction Coloniale/Universal Company of Colonial Construction and by virtue of the decisions taken by the company's board of directors including the architect Mr. Gabriel Duban, I shall strike the first shovel to build an island of civilization here in the East."*

In the next issues, reports of colossal digging began. The engravings showed clusters of workers ordered to pose for the long exposures while gathered around tents. Steam dredges dominated the landscape with massive chimneys billowing smoke like outstretched arms of a spider. The project foreman had published a letter to share his experience: *"I dare say I've never seen anything as big or imposing as those dredgers. Nothing can give a better idea of man's genius and power than to beat the resistance of matter. You see these enormous iron buckets descending in a line and plunging to the bottom of the pits, coming up full of sand, mud, and debris. They're filled to the edge and tipped against a humongous geared wheel that pulverizes the mud and drops it down an enormous chute."*

A couple of weeks after the construction started, numerous skeptics and opponents of the project began to raise their voices in a campaign against it. The Ministry of Colonies was one of the sworn enemies and they accused Gabriel of treason.

THE VICEROY

Gabriel had even come across an interesting passage quoting Girard: *"I warn any French citizens against investment in the Universal Company's venture. I will personally lead a team of investigators to Turkistan to verify the legitimacy of the Universal Company and this supposed viceroy. So far, no one has been able to gain any information about his origins or interests and he most definitely should not be trusted. I'd also like to mention that the Ministry was interested in Duban's design, but we were waiting for the right time to approach him. Now that he's left us to work for Russians, it's obvious where his allegiance lies! He's a traitor and should no longer be called a Frenchman."*

Many of the letters had stirred the worries of those who had placed their capital in the sands of Kokand. Many people were concerned about whether or not the settlement would stand the test of its own weight. Would it be able to handle the incredible gusts of a tempest called "capital of winds" that were recently reported in the area? People also seemed to be interested in whose political interests would be best served. La Patrie wrote: *"Most of the applicants for shares are clerks who've been duped by the firm. The whole business is nothing but robbery inflicted on simple folk who've allowed themselves to be taken in, for not a single penny will ever be collected in tolls from a town that is impossible to build. Duban is engaged in one of the riskiest financial affairs of the century, which appears to be impossible and will certainly end in a catastrophe. For his own good, he must not be allowed to continue."*

Gabriel paid no attention to such critiques as he watched the settlement growing in the daily journal reports. In the third week the first pillar was raised—so tall that it disappeared in the clouds making the engraving difficult to read. In the fourth week a small-scale workers' rebellion occurred, but it was dealt with efficiently and unequivocally after the viceroy threatened to impale a few of the officers. Official representatives from all the European empires, members of the chamber of commerce, and delegates for shareholders took turns visiting and inspecting the site while highlighting the success of the expedition. Their accounts were published every week.

The Journal de la Compagnie summarized one of the delegate's speeches: *"We can therefore safely say that the whole of Europe proclaims and affirms the universal utility of the building of this settlement. It is the beginning of a new era in the colonization of the Far East. Political and commercial representatives have recognized that the suspended city rises above all accusations of having been created for personal ambitions or nationalistic purposes, which were used for discrediting this grand venture of progress."*

CHAPTER
05

Another delegate's chronicle read: "This fantastical voyage was the closest thing to a dream I've ever seen while awake. In fact, seeing truly IS believing! This town-in-the-making is much more than a charming sight. It's breathtaking. Despite its young age, it already covers a considerable area: on the lake sides there are houses, all built on stilts and, on the right, the Khirgiz village inhabited by at least 2,000 to 3,000 people. The place is filled with skeptics who've come from all over the world to see it with their own eyes!" And a caption underneath a particularly large engraving stated: "A pavilion has been erected especially for the viceroy and at his request; the triumphal arch and Venetian poles await his forthcoming arrival. Nearby stands a platform decorated with flags and palms where the celebration is to be held."

On May 15 Gabriel's assistant entered his office and told him that the delivery of news from the colony had been delayed and he wasn't able to gain any new information from the viceroy or about the progress of the city. The journal had gone out of print.

CHAPTER 06

SUNSET
WALKING HOME
MAY 17ᵗʰ SEINE

GABRIEL WAS WALKING HOME FROM THE OFFICE WHEN HE NOTICED THAT THE SKY ABOVE THE SEINE HAD BECOME A GLOWING, ORANGE MASS. SOMETHING THAT LOOKED LIKE A TRAIL OF SMOKE ROSE INTO THE CLOUDS AND THE SURROUNDING BRIDGES WERE DARK SILHOUETTES FLOATING IN BETWEEN. He wondered if a building had caught fire near the office. At five-thirty he walked through the door to his home only to be greeted by Marianne's stunned expression. Her eyes were wide open and she tried to talk but nothing came out. Then she broke into a strangled laughter and held up a letter. "What have you done to us?" "What are you talking about?" asked Gabriel. "Stop your ugly games!" His stomach turned. He repeated above a whisper, "What are you talking about?" "This letter," she screamed, "is from the bank and our balance is zero! That check from the viceroy was a fake. We haven't received money for over two weeks. The construction was abandoned and the company went bankrupt!" Gabriel snatched the envelope away from her and began reading furiously, dropping it on the floor as finished. "There must be some mistake!" "I also know you were fired, you liar!" Marianne started sobbing again. "Why couldn't you just have stayed at the Ministry?" she choked. Gabriel sat down, his face in his hands. "This is impossible! It's utter nonsense; I've been following the reports every day at work! Things are advancing fine!

Look here, the pillars are already standing." He pulled out the journal from his briefcase. "Look at this, and this." He pointed to the engravings. "You, monster!" she cried and started hitting his chest and shoulders with her open palms. Gabriel didn't try to defend himself. Finally she collapsed on the sofa, sobbing until a shriek broke out from Daniel's room. "This can't be the truth," mumbled Gabriel. "Truth! How dare you talk about truth? What else have you been hiding from me? I already know you lied

to me about the Ministry, so that means the dinner party was also a lie as well as the promotion and now this! Who were you meeting, Gabriel?" Her voice was contemptuous. "Was it a woman? You and your goddamn company! I hope your colony goes to hell!" She ran into Daniel's room and Gabriel followed.

He watched as she took their crying son from the cradle and began rocking him in her arms. Gabriel put his hand on her shoulder, caressed her forehead and whispered, "Marianne everything's going to be okay. I'll fix it. I promise. The venture has many enemies. You shouldn't believe them." "Oh god, who should I believe?" she said weakly as she thrust herself and the baby into his arms.

Caressing her hair, he tried to remind himself how much he loved both of them. "I'm sure it's all due to communication problems, I'll fix this. Nothing is lost, there hasn't been anyone at the company yet…" His voice trailed off. "The company!" Gabriel said to himself. "Please wait, I'm going there to find out about all this!" Before Marianne could say another word, Gabriel rushed out of the room.

CHAPTER
06

A mob had assembled in front of the offices and they were buzzing like an angry beehive. A bonfire had been built in the middle of the square and people were yelling about their investments. Some held sticks or torches. Police had cordoned off the building and Gabriel kept his distance, pulling down his hat, so as not to be recognized. A few feet away he heard a gendarme asking an officer what was happening. "We can't disclose anything, please keep moving," was the reply. *"TELL DUBAN WE WANT OUR MONEY BACK OR WE'LL BURN HIM AT THE STAKE!"* The random threat echoed over the crowd and Gabriel backed into the shadows.

Around twilight the crowd had dispersed and he rounded the corner to enter a neighboring building. He surreptitiously crossed the courtyard and hopped over a fence that led to the company garden. Gabriel knew that a bathroom window on the first floor of the building had a ledge, so he climbed onto a garbage bin and grasped hold of it. With a powerful lunge, he smashed the window with his elbow, causing a loud blast that echoed throughout the trees.

Gabriel froze and tried to crouch in the shadows as he hung in an unusual position on the side of the building. He waited with bated breath until his fingers grew so numb he had no choice but to drop or climb inside. The window was so small he had to crawl in head first before landing heavily on his shoulder. He got up, regained his balance, and headed through the hallways, which he knew very well. Some lights were on and he thought he heard muffled voices behind a closed door, so he froze and waited until they disappeared before continuing on through the building. There were various objects scattered around the floor such as bits of paper, stamps, and miscellaneous books. The carpet was askew and wrinkled. Gabriel noticed scratch lines across the wooden paneling as if someone had been dragging a big animal.

As he passed through the ballroom where the party had been held, he found it bare except for a few big pieces of furniture, formless hulks covered in white sheets. The colonial decorations were gone. There was only the smell of dust settling in the air. Gabriel kept asking himself if it was really the same building, when he suddenly felt something warm and sticky running down his right arm. He glanced down and saw that his sleeve was soaked with blood and large drops were blooming like brightly colored rose petals onto the floor. "Funny, I didn't even feel a thing." A wave of nausea came over him. With a deep breath, he took off his coat and wrapped it tightly around his forearm and he continued on. He finally reached his office and found the door gaping open to reveal a scene of frenetic disarray. Furniture lay strewn about.

Chairs were upturned and there was a half-filled suitcase sprawling out on the floor. All the pictures were torn from the walls and broken frames lay among the wreckage. Several drawings were perched on the desk or rested in a swirl on the floor. Loose freehand sketches, top views that looked like stars, others like flowers or hieroglyphs with tribal symbols, were interspersed throughout. The air was heavy. On his desk was a letter from Senna:

Dear Gabriel,
The viceroy has decided to run things differently than planned. Unexpected circumstances have arisen, which require your immediate attention at the settlement. Although, I've been told otherwise, the press has gotten word that the company is bankrupt. Do not stay in Paris! As soon as the newspapers reach the stands, you'll be pinpointed as a scapegoat and the whole city will be at your throat. Don't worry, the viceroy is a genius and everything is going according to plan.
Yours truly,
Senna

Attached to the letter was a thick package full of photographs depicting the structure in the final stages of completion. He thumbed through them with a smile as he recognized the shots he hadn't yet seen. There was one of Orlof standing next to a row of dark spherical objects balancing on long pikes. Gabriel threw the package under his arm and snuck out of the office. The exit door was open. With his hat tilted downward and his face pushed into his scarf, he furtively walked around to the front of the building and onto the street when he heard a voice from the square. "This was the venture of the century, alright." He turned around to see Jacob holding a small flintlock pistol. "So, Gabriel, how's the viceroy? Obviously Turkistan was an excellent choice for me to spend the last of my money." Gabriel stepped back. "It's all lies, Jacob. I have a letter right here in my pocket," he said, slowly reaching into his coat. "Too late, old friend. I'm already a dead man." Jacob raised the pistol just below his chin. There was a blast and blood sprayed out of his eyes.

Gabriel stood motionless for a moment as the sound of the shot ricocheted off the buildings. His eyes were empty as he turned on his heels and walked away.

"What happened, you're bleeding!" said Marianne when he stumbled through the door. Gabriel said nothing as she grabbed his arm and led him to the kitchen.

"What happened?" she asked again. "Don't worry. Things are a little messed up. I wasn't careful enough. I know I put you and Daniel at risk but I'll fix it. Everything will be fine." He opened Senna's package and spread the photos all over the floor. "Gabriel, what happened to your arm!" Marianne asked him again. "I cut myself on some broken glass when I snuck into the company. It appears I took things into my own hands." Gabriel points back to the photos. "Look, the construction was continued and now it's almost complete." Marianne hesitated before kneeling down and looking at the images.

"See, all four pillars are erected!" She leaned up against him, bending to look at the dim print. "And look here," said Gabriel. "The large platform's already been mounted... here are the dates. Trust me, this is real." "Gabriel, these images are blurry. I can't see a thing." "I'm going to Turkistan!" "No, you're not!" "Look, Marianne, there have been rumors that Orlof may not be with the Russian Empire. They say he's either a crook or a vicious warlord who will set the region on fire. I have to go there." "Why?" "To prove my innocence. All the stockholders are ruined. Tomorrow I'll be martyred. The judges, the police, the entire city will be at my heels. I know the construction is finished, so I'll either get back what's ours or destroy the whole goddamn city." "You're delusional!" "No, I'm not! I know where the keystone is. I can bring that city to the ground. I will find Orlof and make the bastard pay me." Marianne rose to her feet. "Let me see your arm, we have to clean it." "Forget about the arm. I gotta pack." "Gabriel, you're not going anywhere." There was an unusual inflection in her voice. "Let's just forget this nightmare and let the General Security deal with it." "No, Marianne, they're useless and I'm leaving tonight." He paced by the window, his thoughts racing. "Gabriel you're an architect, not some kind of explorer. Do you realize how far away that country is?" "I have no choice." Her voice grew tired and quiet. She begged him, "But what about your son and me? You'll leave us alone and broke? Don't you love me anymore? What have we done to deserve this?" Her look of supplication would have moved harder men than Gabriel, but he stood silent with his hand pressed to his forehead. His eyes were fixed on the eastern horizon. Marianne got close, pressed her body against him, kissed his face and neck, and breathed in his ear, "Please!" But, Gabriel remained motionless for a while, and then as if returning, he said with deep sincerity, "I love you both, more than anything in the world, but I'm going. Staying here would be like committing suicide." She let go of him, sat down resigned, and said more to herself than her husband, "I guess that's what you've always wanted, isn't it?" Gabriel marched into the next room and began packing his shirts, sweaters, and boots. As he tried to shut the suitcase, things kept popping out of the sides. Marianne watched him struggle and finally intervened. "Gabriel, stop it. That's not how it's done." She pulled him aside. "Here, let me help you. I'll rearrange everything and it'll close easily."

He let her do it and proceeded to pack his best drawing kit; a beautiful mahogany and ivory case he'd received as a birthday present from his father. It had smooth chambers in the shape of various drafting tools. He carefully examined the carved ivory handles as he laid down a brass straight edge, silver and steel tubular compasses, a beam compass, a brass and porcelain horn valuator, an ebony and pearwood pantograph, and other strangely shaped instruments. Everything about them was designed for precision and they glinted like surgical instruments as he snapped them into their beds. Gabriel clicked shut the lock and held the kit in his hands. "Are you sure you need that?" asked Marianne doubtfully. Gabriel was silent as she handed him a small silver cross on a chain. "I know you don't believe in God, but take it anyway." She fixed the buttons on his jacket and straightened his collar. Gabriel kissed her and without another word he left the room.

Gabriel boarded at the Gare de l'Est on a second-class coach to Constantinople and sat alone in the compartment. Looking through the window he followed the cigarette butts, tickets, and luggage chariots as they slowly slid away. The monotonous shaking of handkerchiefs on the platform matched the rhythm of the pistons.

The silhouette of his wife and son were shrinking steadily behind him and he never realized how much Marianne looked like a fragile child from a distance. For a moment he felt a weight on his chest and he couldn't breathe. He wanted to jump from the train and run back to them, but he regained control of himself.

The platform passed by him, followed by houses and churches. Then the entire faubourgs slipped away in a blur. A series of darkened tunnels and flashes of morning sky were replaced by fields, and a yellow haze absorbed everything. Gabriel leaned his head against the window and drifted off into dreams.

CHAPTER 07

TRAVEL CONSTANTINOPLE IN SEARCH OF LOST CITY

A WAVY SEA OF WHITE AND BRIGHTLY COLORED HOUSES· ABOVE WHICH ROSE THE MIGHTY CUPOLAS AND THE TALL SLENDER MINARETS· Headed for Kokand in the path of the viceroy and his lost city,

Gabriel boarded the Russian ship Rostov Odessa and steamed out through the Bosporus
with the European coast on the left and the Asiatic on the right. On all sides of the
Rostov was a landscape of peculiar beauty as the ship glided out onto black sea.
He landed at Batumi and went by rail via Tiflis to Baku. On his way to the Caspian
Sea a fantastic spectacle struck him: the Nobel oil fields at Baku-—the "Black City.
"There were 310 wells gushing thousands of pounds of crude oil that were piped into
the town daily. White flames rose from the black city, dense brown clouds belching
above them. With a chill Gabriel recognized an engraving of "Dante's Inferno" come to
life. A premonition? His heart tightened. But he had not chosen to be here—this was
the road.

Gabriel learned that the viceroy and his men had passed through the city, loading
barrels of the precious fluid on their caravan. A fight between a guard and an oil worker
had broken out. Before leaving, Orlof's soldiers had set ablaze the lake of crude oil and
burned the derricks. Tatars were still trying to choke the fire with earth, but in vain.

In the heart of Asia Minor Gabriel crossed street lanes crowded with camels, mules, vehicles, and people of various races: Russians, Armenians, Tatars, Georgians, Circassians, Persians, Gypsies, and Jews. He discovered places with magical names like Ashkhabad, and the Kara-Kum Desert with its hot black sands. There he lost the trace of the viceroy. Questioning, investigating, he was drawn farther and farther toward the East. He learned to mount mules, camels, and horses. He followed caravans, wandering dervishes, and Bedouins in the lands of the terrible Tamerlane. Desolate landscapes were enveloped in clouds of mist. Often when the haze lifted, instead of the wealth and splendor of Arabian nights, he saw just common clay houses and palm trees. In the Elburz Mountains he fought and escaped three Khirgiz robbers.

He was on the ancient Silk Road when he picked up the trail of the viceroy again. From every village Orlof had been taking boys and young men by force, while others joined his army by their own free will. One boy from every ten houses, but the numbers changed day to day. Boys age 14 to 18 were preferred, though younger ones were taken too. Gabriel would hear stories about Orlof's supernatural powers and cold cruelty. "Whom am I following?" he wondered. "A warlord with a horde of mercenaries? A crazy prophet? A common marauder? What about my city?"

Then he saw the viceroy's work with his own eyes. On a crisp, clear morning he entered a village and saw an entire population slaughtered and thrown onto a pile because a mother refused to give up her son. Despite his sickness and horror Gabriel's determination grew. He knew he had to shed blood if he wanted the viceroy.

By December, an armed outfit of anti-Russian Turkmen tribesmen captured Gabriel. They spared his life to use him as a spy because of his European face and blond hair, turned almost white from the steppe sun. He played along because it fit his plan and they had the same destination: Kokand.

PART
02

DOES ANYONE KNOW THE WHEREABOUTS OF THE COMPAGNIE UNIVERSALLE OFFICES?

CHAPTER
08

HEAT
TRAIN TO
KOKAND
AT STATION

THE LIGHT WAS BOUNCING OFF THE GROUND AS IF THE WORLD WERE FLIPPED UPSIDE DOWN. EVERYTHING IN KOKAND WAS COVERED IN A UNIFORM FILM OF GRAY-WHITISH DUST. GABRIEL YANKED HIS MULE OFF THE CARGO WAGON OF THE TRAIN. Gabriel yanked his mule off the cargo wagon of the train. The station was a shack of corrugated metal and wood and peeling strips of paint erupted from the sides. Rabid dogs were skulking along the platform with glowing eyes and something about their movement seemed human, like Gabriel was surrounded by a pack of demons. He had become accustomed to the heat and the sun burning against the sky like a Cyclops's eye. Gabriel was enveloped in an inescapable misery and yet he was too weak to be disappointed in the dismal town that lay before him. Smiling maliciously, he heard himself break down into a vicious laughter and he wondered, why? As he found himself staring into the shattered face of his surroundings, he felt no comfort, and his outburst only made him uneasy.

He was a wreck. He had to get a hold of himself. Once again he took a deep breath and recounted his already remarkable journey; something he'd gotten in the habit of doing when he felt all hope had abandoned him. Slowly he dragged his mule through the deserted streets. The blasting sun continued to bleach the surrounding buildings

an unnatural white and he noticed the heat had a peculiar way of curling and distorting the architecture, turning the structures into grotesque mounds of broken eggshells. There was an abandoned market to his left and a bunch of old women were crouching in the shadows selling dried violet fruits. A dead horse swarming with gnats eyed Gabriel from the gutter as he maneuvered around a pile of rotten melons. His mule crushed one of them splattering moldy juice in every direction. The sound spooked a nearby sheep and Gabriel watched it dart in front of him and clamber over a vertical rock wall. This certainly wasn't the Oriental dream he had had in mind.

As he walked past the ramshackle houses, he saw an old man slam shut the window of a nearby building. At a watering hole, a granny shielded the heads of a couple filthy children who watched him in fascination. The locals looked ragged and hostile, and when Gabriel tried to ask them about the Company they simply walked off in the other direction. All he could see were women, elderly couples, and young children roaming the streets and he wondered what had happened to the workforce.

Eventually he entered what looked like the town square. He saw dozens of dark spherical objects on the ends of long white poles. It took him a moment to realize that they were hardened human heads skewered on pikes while flies shrouded them in a black mist. There was a yellow and turquoise fountain in the center; its side had been blown away, probably by dynamite. Gabriel struggled walking through smashed mosaics and mud puddles caused by the water that continued to trickle from a bent pipe in the center.On the far end of the square he saw an old man and called out to him, but he didn't answer. He stepped around the miniature pond next to the fountain and cautiously approached him asking directions in every language he could muster. Mostly he tried using the Russian he'd been studying on the road. There was no reply. Gabriel grabbed the old man's arm and shook him, but he murmured something in the unintelligible local dialect and hobbled away. Behind him, Gabriel heard the sound of a marching band playing a sad dirge-like tune in an off, Asiatic scale. A meager funeral procession appeared from around the corner of a building. There were a couple of older boys shouldering coffins and Gabriel ran toward them. "Can somebody please tell me what happened here?" he begged. "Does anyone know the whereabouts of the Compagnie Universelle offices?"

A tall, broad-shouldered boy with a tear-streaked face looked up at Gabriel with hate and shoved him backward. Gabriel tripped and felt the sting of wet sand in his eyes as a wall of mud splashed up around him. He struggled to get up when a couple of children began taunting him in an incomprehensible language that sounded like mock French.

When he got up the children stepped back and started hawking up globs of spit and launching them at him from a distance. One of the kids started throwing stones and Gabriel had to cover his head. By the time he got up they had already fled between the houses.

By the time he'd finished washing his boots in the fountain and drying off his clothes, it was already beginning to get dark. He put on his muddy shirt and watched the sun sink below the horizon. The sunset painted pictures in the sky, leaving the whole town shrouded in a purple glow. Exhaustion had overtaken Gabriel, and he realized he needed to find a place to sleep before it got dark or he would be in for a bitterly cold evening. After a quick scan, he took the next biggest street in the square. Before long he heard a sad Russian melody from a slightly out-of-tune accordion in a tavern down the road. Wearily, he pulled his legs in the direction of the sound. When he arrived, the song had reached its climax and he was standing in front of a strange neo-Asiatic drinking establishment made of stucco and tiles. The tail end of the structure was buried beneath the sand and a tall dune rose up behind it. There used to be what looked like a vending window in front, but it had long since been boarded up and the only entrance was a Mongolian-style doorway covered by an Oriental rug. He tied his mule to a gnarled tree root and sauntered inside.

CHAPTER
08

At the bar sat two ragged Russian soldiers and an officer with his hat flipped sideways who played a small accordion. The officer gazed off into space with a sparkling glint in his eye and a majestic red mustache that recounted the wisdom of a seasoned military official. Although he wavered drunkenly he never missed a note. He somehow seemed familiar and Gabriel tried to remember where he had seen him before. High cheek-boned locals sat scattered around the tavern drinking tea and sucking on water pipes. Smoke hung thick in the air and fat bearded men lay passed out on the tables with stupefied looks plastered on their faces. Others were outstretched on pillows as if they hadn't moved for days.

Exhausted, Gabriel pulled up a stool and sat down at the bar next to the Russian soldiers. Everyone seemed to be looking at him, but his ragged appearance, dirty duster, and travel-worn boots made him feel comfortable in the gritty tavern. "Vodka, please," Gabriel said to the bartender in a gravelly voice as he took out his pipe and began searching his pockets for some matches. One of the Russian soldiers leaned over and cupped a flame in his palm. Gabriel lit the ivory bowl and took a couple puffs. "Merci," he said as he let the smoke drift into the air like a dying a steam engine. "French?" asked the soldier in Russian. "Yeah, my Russian's very poor," said Gabriel in his native tongue as he noticed the other soldier peering at him with an opium-ridden smile. He nodded politely. After all, these were the first people he'd been able to communicate with all day. Their uniforms were filthywhite, and looked like they hadn't been taken off for a year.

For a minute they said nothing and Gabriel wondered if he'd somehow offended them when all of a sudden the second soldier said jokingly in French, "Don't worry, he's a German. He barely speaks Russian." His friend started laughing in a deep booming voice that filled the air and caused the passed-out locals to stir. When he was finished, the German turned back to Gabriel and held out his hand, "I am Franz and I am speaking French and Russian, but he made a joke because my native tongue is German." He tells truth," said his friend in between gasps of intoxicated laughter. When he finally regained control of himself, he stretched out his hand to greet Gabriel. "Where'd you learn to speak French?" "We happened to have a business trip in Paris, a mission," said Franz. "Well, you better tell him we were stationed in Paris until La Compagnie ordered us here." They spoke in third person making a mockery of Gabriel's politeness. Gabriel was irritated, but kept cool. "But La Compagnie gets its orders from the viceroy, no?" "What viceroy? Do you know any viceroys Volodya? Maybe you know the czar's wife?" Franz asked his friend with a big smile. Vladimir shook his head animatedly.

"I never met no viceroys," he said as he grabbed Gabriel by the arm. Gabriel immediately slid his hand into his pocket and wrapped his fingers around a knife he'd bought in Constantinople, but a cherub baby smile broke out on Vladimir's face. Apparently it was only soldier's humor and Gabriel watched tears rolling down the Russian's cheeks. He got up and kissed him with a wet smack on the mouth and Gabriel was so startled he let go of the knife. Vladimir put his arms around him and pulled him close. He could feel his breath on his ear as he began to whisper, "Mon frère, bratushka! Why so jumpy? Everything's fine." Gabriel tried to pull back, but the hug tightened and he felt his ribs contract. In the corner of his eye he saw Franz holding up a stool ready to smash him in the back. He struggled to get free, but Vladimir held him like a grizzly bear. A bang. The chair splintered over his spine and an intense pain shot through his body like a bolt of lighting. Then he felt his knees give in.

In a daze, Gabriel heard the accordion music stop. There was a clicking noise as the officer clipped shut the instrument and his heavy footsteps got louder. He was a foot taller than everyone else in the room. Volodia released Gabriel and took a step back, but the

Officer grabbed him and smacked him on the back of the neck as hard as he could. Franz tried to go for his gun, but he was too slow on the draw and the officer bashed him in the forehead like a ram. Blood spurted from his temple and splattered Gabriel in the face. He wiped it from his eyes and took in the scene as the officer dealt out several hefty kicks to both the soldiers who were writhing on the ground. When he was finished, he took both the pistols from their holsters and handed one to Gabriel. The officer slid the other gun under his belt, smiled, and said something in a strange language. Then he unhooked his accordion and continued playing. His stained fingers smeared the men's blood across the broken keys as he disappeared behind the rug covering the entrance. Gabriel looked down at Franz as he gurgled and spit out a tooth. The sound of the officer's voice wavered down the street

as he stumbled down the street and, all of a sudden, Gabriel remembered where he'd seen him. He approached the officer at a distance and realized he wasn't singing in Russian, and he tried to place the dialect. It was from the north—Finnish or Estonian. Gabriel started to wonder whom this strange man was working for. It was no coincidence that he was in Kokand, because he was absolutely sure it was the tall architect he'd seen at the Ministry. "Why'd you do that?" Without turning around, the officer replied in a very fine accented French. "Because otherwise you'd be dead." "Why?" The officer laughed. "Well, maybe they wanted you dead." "I remember you dressed up as an architect at the competition, the one who stood up for me." Gabriel tried to catch up to him when a couple shouts echoed from the tavern. He whirled around only to see Volodia lurch through the entrance. He pulled a small revolver from his boot, crossed himself and held up the gun. "Duuuuuck!" Gabriel yelled as he lunged at the officer. He heard a gunshot in midair and felt a sharp sting in his right arm that quickly elevated into an excruciating burn. He'd been shot. Instinctively Gabriel rolled over on the street and clutched his arm in agony as he watched the officer put a bullet in the Russian's head. At once, Franz hopped out of the tavern with his hands up and inched toward his dead friend. He hadn't moved an arm's length before the officer let off another shot, shitting the German in the shoulder and the chest. The soldier staggered backward and landed behind Gabriel's mule, which nervously kicked at the quivering corpse. Gabriel watched his blood dripping onto the street and he clutched his arm even tighter. He nodded in and out of consciousness as the officer quickly propped him up and tore off his shirtsleeve to stop the bleeding. Gabriel felt the pressure of the knotted shirt on his arm and his heart began to pound as he felt himself being lifted up. The officer led them toward a side street and the last thing he could remember was a bloody accordion lying in the street.

YOU DON'T JUST GO THERE. YOU ALONE HAVE A CHANCE OF REACHING THE CITY.

CHAPTER 09

MORNING
INJURED
ARM
DOG HUNGER

GABRIEL AWOKE TO THE SOUND OF THE OFFICER SINGING ANOTHER STRANGE SONG. HE BLINKED AND LOOKED DOWN AT HIS ARM ONLY TO SEE IT WAS ALL PROPERLY BANDAGED. SLOWLY HE EXAMINED THE PLACE. He was lying on a bed in what looked like a shabby Oriental-style hotel room. His eyes focused on the officer as he washed what appeared to be medical tools in a basin by his bed. Gabriel blinked a couple times and noticed they were instruments from his drafting kit.

"I guess I won't be drawing anytime soon," said Gabriel in a hoarse whisper. The officer looked over at him with a smile. "Not unless you're good with your left arm." "Who were those men?" asked Gabriel. "Soldiers," he said with a shrug. "Yeah, but whom were they working for?" "Don't know. Everything's gotten a bit hazy around here since the construction stopped. No one seems to know anything anymore." "So I guess … the viceroy's found out I'm here? Have people been waiting for me?" "Who knows? The man works in mysterious ways." "What do you know about him?" "I joined his army when Skobelev left. Life in the imperial ranks left a bitter taste in my mouth and the viceroy gave me a perfect offer." "So if he's gone, then where'd those soldiers get their orders? Aren't you their superior?" The officer smiled grimly. "No orders anymore because there are no sides. The viceroy's moved on, and this town's just a leftover on his warpath."

81

"What are you talking about?" The officer dismissed his question. "You hungry?" But Gabriel pressed on. "Please, just tell me what happened to the construction!" He tried pulling himself up, but his arm burned with a searing pain as he fell back on the sheets. The officer tossed a roasted animal leg on his chest. "Eat first, talk later." Gabriel eyed the piece of meat and he could not resist. He grabbed it with his left hand and tore into it. It was much tougher than he expected and the taste was a surprise. "Bitter meat. What is it?" "Kara-Kum Desert dog," replied the officer in all seriousness. Gabriel gulped, but he was so hungry he didn't care. The officer continued, "You see the construction poisoned most of the cattle and many dogs were overtaken by the restless spirits of workers who weren't ready to leave this world. By killing them, I free their souls from limbo."

Gabriel didn't reply. He had already understood that the farther east he went, the more magic, superstition, and ghosts appeared. He forgot at what point he had let go of reality and allowed magic in. "Why not eat the goats I saw wondering around the station?" "Because the locals would kill me," the officer said, smiling softly to himself as he filled his pipe with a rich blend of Turkish tobacco. He lit a match and took a puff. "So you want to know about the Company, eh?" Gabriel nodded with his mouth full as he thought of the officer's appearance. He had a stern yet melancholic disposition. "Orlof was set on building a new kingdom around here and wanted to expand it east and west. With your design complete, the place would be unconquerable." The officer exhaled. "We started building not far from town. The locals were forced to work in bad conditions.

82

Very bad. A huge number starved, fell, or were beaten to death. There were rebellions and executions. The lucky ones were impaled and the unlucky ones were taken to the local offices and nobody, not even their families, ever saw or spoke to them again. The oneswho returned had their eyes and their tongues ripped out. At night, bodies were stacked up around the edges of the construction site and the dogs would carry off their bones." The officer put his feet up and carefully watched Gabriel's reaction.

"So what happened to the rest of the workers?" The officer took several sturdy puffs of his pipe tobacco. "They were taken away. Some of the chief officers were told to stay behind with their men to oversee the migration, but when the workers disappeared, that's when I decided to get out and it nearly cost me my head. I was very lucky I got away with this." He moved some hair away from the side of his head and a flat, ugly hole full of scar tissue was all that was left of his ear. Gabriel winced. "No one escapes from the viceroy without something to show for it." "Then what about the leftover soldiers?" "A gang of Russian Army deserters arrived and took over the town. They turned this place into a hole for marauders, headhunters, merchants, and war profiteers. Tensions arose between tribes and the outcome was a series of bloody battles especially with the Khirgiz and the Tatars." "So where exactly where the workers taken?" "To finish building your settlement, it had to be relocated. The viceroy failed to put it here in Kokand, so he was forced to move it to the only other place in the world where it could be built." "And where's that?" "Beyond the Company offices lay a hidden valley and a black salt lake. On the other side of the lake there is a place where no human has entered and returned alive. That's where the viceroy has settled." "Fine, then take me there." "No human, bird, animal, nothing has escaped from that place. You don't just go there. Believe me I'd get rid of Orlof myself if I had the chance. But you, Gabriel, you have a contract with the man. Of all projects, the viceroy chose yours. You alone have a chance of reaching the city and that's precisely why I'm telling you to give up." "No! Now that's out of the question! Remember, it's my city! I came all the way over here to findOrlof and finish our business." "I can see you're a stubborn Frenchman." "I need a guide. I'll pay you." "Pay me!" the officer laughed. "This desert has given me a crude oil reserve big enough to cover the cost of your construction myself!" "And what are YOU doing here then?" yelled Gabriel. The officer sighed. "It's not fortune or money. I too have my mission to complete." Gabriel waited. "A heavy one," he said, followed by another long pause. "Observe, witness, and chronicle this." "This?" "Yes. Not your story, for it is just a fragment mine. I must keep track of events because an era is coming to an end. Orlof is the main character of my writings. It's my duty to document it all.

ONLY ONE ANCHORAGE FOR THE STEEL CABLES OF THE CITY HAD BEEN BUILT.

CHAPTER
09

Drifting, changing camps and armies, I was the only one to see all sides of the story and tell it well. That's why I became a soldier and a deserter—to keep a better journal." "Your duty?" Gabriel asked. "You see, a new era is approaching. Prophecies will soon be fulfilled. The world will be purified though fire. Good and evil will clash, bleed, dance together, and become one. The old world is dead. Civilization will crumble. The viceroy may be the one who brings the change. Or somebody else. And I must be patient and resistant because I must witness and chronicle because all traces will be erased. And now you walked into my story and became a part of it." Gabriel replied, "I didn't come here to die or to be a part of your chronicles. My reputation and family are at stake. Why else would anyone travel to this hellhole? And what if none of this is worth seeing or chronicling? What if oases turn out to be nothing more than a pissholes in the sand?" "Then you're too foolish to realize it was a mirage in the first place. Everything is." Gabriel asked, "What are you? A mystic? A fakir? A desert madman?" The officer smiled at Gabriel as he eyed the silver cross on his neck. "Well, I certainly never took YOU for a religious man." Gabriel sensed the sarcasm, and when he realized the officer was looking at his necklace he laughed. "Oh, that! My wife gave it to me." "Whether you're religious or not is no concern of mine. What interests me is that you're a new chapter in my story. You're named after the archangel, a being said to bring truth and unity to all things."

Just as Gabriel was beginning to get tired with the officer's esoteric talk, the man slowly rose to his feet and headed for the exit. "Where are you going?" asked Gabriel. "To sleep, and you should do the same. You've got a long road ahead if you're going to reach those offices." With that, the officer disappeared through the doorway and Gabriel watched as the lock clicked shut behind him. Gabriel suddenly felt exhausted and he almost instantly sank back and drifted off to sleep.

That night he was plagued by nightmares. He was sitting at his drawing table, but instead of walls he was in the vast expanse of rolling sand dunes. His right arm hung limp at his side and he was diligently trying to use a metal protractor with his left hand. This wasn't an easy task and the sheet of paper before him was covered with unfinished circles. A gust of wind filled his inkbottle with sand and a huge stain started expanding across the page. The stack of papers filled the air and a teepee appeared in front of him. He looked over and saw the flap open up.

Marianne came running out and she sat down at Gabriel's feet, her hands raised in prayer. He knew she was begging for him to listen, but he heard no sound from her lips. Instead, Gabriel looked away and continued working with his protractor.

She grabbed his arm and he brusquely pushed her away, accidentally stabbed her with the sharp point of his protractor. He felt like he'd delivered a fatal sting and Marianne held her wrist as a drop of blood welled up on the back of her hand. He watched helplessly as she crumpled to the floor and stopped breathing.

His arm began to burn from the bullet wound and he dropped the protractor as a trickle of blood leaked through the fabric. He tore open his shirt, saw the open bullet hole, and closed his eyes in anguish. Suddenly his pain turned to panic when he felt something crawling up his left arm. He tried to move, but he was frozen in place. He watched in horror as a black, fat-tailed scorpion crawled out of his sleeve and onto his forearm. The arachnid positioned its venomous sting over the open wound and Gabriel noticed his eyes had begun to water. He watched helplessly as the scorpion plunged its barbed tail inside the bullet hole. His vision blurred as he felt the deadly venom surge through his veins like a lethal injection and a great white light appeared before him.

CHAPTER 10

STORM

SCORPION
EXPOSED

SURVIVED

GABRIEL AWOKE IN A DAZE AND IT WAS UNCLEAR HOW LONG HE'D BEEN OUT. BUT IT FELT LIKE IT WAS NEARLY TWO DAYS. HIS ARM ACHED AND SOMETHING TOLD HIM TO CHANGE THE BANDAGES. HE GOT UP. FOUND A PAIR OF SILVER SHEARS ON HIS BEDSIDE TABLE. AND SNIPPED OFF THE BANDAGE. Beneath the stained cotton, the bloody hole had almost closed up and he noticed some kind of organic brown mixture was smeared in a ring around the maimed flesh.

"That officer's a goddamn witch doctor," he muttered under his breath as he tested the use of his aching muscles. No more fever. Either way, the wound looked much better, so he rinsed it off with some water from the washbasin across the room and looked for the bandages. Nearby he spotted a roll of white gauze and he carefully tried to unfold it using only one hand. He still couldn't lift his right arm so he had to use his teeth, but after a bit of a struggle he managed get the bandage tightly wrapped around the wound. After a short breather, he put on a clean shirt and walked downstairs.

The corridors and rooms looked pretty shabby, but the building itself seemed to expand. When Gabriel got downstairs he found an unkempt check-in desk with a rusty bell on the table. He hammered it a couple times but no one showed up. While waiting, he turned around to examine the grand dining room. It was full of overturned chairs and a smashed piano dotted with bullet holes leaned up against a wall. He figured the hotel must've been a battleground. As he inspected a couple of black stains on the wall, he heard a voice from behind him.

"What do you want?" asked a gangly Georgian who stepped out of a caged-off backroom behind the counter. "I was wondering if you could tell me what happened to the man who brought me here?" "I told officer you stay here only because I owe him favor. But if you make trouble, then I feed you to dogs." "Fine then. Do you know anyone who could take me to the Company offices? I have money to pay a guide." The hotel owner watched Gabriel with the eyes of a weasel before he continued. "Officer told me you ask many questions, so I answer you straight." Gabriel perked up his ears. "Only one worker came back from construction site when there was migration. He was last person to see viceroy and he live with wife, two houses down." He gestured with his hand. "Maybe she let you speak to husband, maybe not. I will take you and we will see."

When they reached the house, Gabriel saw a woman leading a man from the dilapidated building. The hotel owner pointed to the couple and told Gabriel to talk to the wife. Gabriel approached her guardedly. "Excuse me, madam, may I please speak to your husband?" The woman kept walking. He tried again. "Excuse me, madam!"

When she wouldn't answer the second time, Gabriel grabbed the man and spun him around. He was blind and both his eyes looked like boiled eggs. When he opened his mouth Gabriel saw his tongue was missing and he let out a gurgling moan as he reached for Gabriel's arm. Gabriel stepped back and he covered his head as the woman began flailing her arms at him. "Goddamn you!" she repeated over and over again and Gabriel came to the realization that this was probably the only phrase she knew in French. He shoved her away and marched back toward the hotel owner in a rage. Gabriel watched him as he broke down into irrepressible laughter. "You see! Now you still wanna go to offices, Frenchman? That's what's gonna happen to you!" the man barked.

CHAPTER
10

Gabriel was almost at the end of his rope and he took out his pocket book waving half of his money in front of the owner. "Find me a guide, right now." The man sneered and picked up the wad of money. "This gets you three-quarters across desert; you need to pay more to get to offices." Gabriel took out all of the remaining bills in his wallet. The owner pocketed the money in his grimy shirt pocket and beckoned for him to follow. "Come with me, Frenchman."

They crossed the street and entered a slum. Broken buildings and collapsed beams from another destroyed marketplace blackened out most of the sky as they wove through shady alleyways. Clotheslines covered in ragged fabric twisted down the curved streets and he saw a man with a sweet smelling pipe disappear in the shadows as they passed into a square full of brothels. A patch of brown palm trees hung limp in the center. Several young prostitutes fanned themselves with large green leaves as the hotel owner led him inside. Silk veils covered the young girls' faces and Gabriel could hear them giggling as they spoke to each other in whispers.

Finally they mounted a spiral staircase and entered an attic. In between mounds of Turkish-style rugs, broken oil lamps, and silver trays of half-eaten meat, Gabriel found his desert guide. There sat a tall, big-boned peasant in the center of the room grilling up some lamb. Gabriel's mouth began to water. He was starving. The hotel owner approached the man with half of the money in his hand and explained in the local dialect what Gabriel wanted. He watched as the guide flashed him a broken smile and took the banknotes. The owner bounced back over to Gabriel and explained the transaction. "Kosma says he takes you when he's finished eating."

It was around one o'clock when Gabriel had readied his mule for the journey. He went to fill an extra canteen of water but Kosma the guide waved his arm signaling that there wouldn't be any need for extra provisions. Without any further communication, Kosma mounted his mule and rode off. Gabriel had to struggle into his saddle, but he managed to get up with only one arm. He watched as the guide moseyed ahead and he pulled at the mule's reigns to catch up. The beast knew what to do and it leisurely trotted after the silhouette ahead.

The road was long and tedious and the sky began to darken as they arrived at a sand dune. Gabriel watched as Kosma turned around smiling and pointing ahead. His heart skipped a few beats as he realized they were close. Gabriel's mind raced with anticipation and he urged his mule forward. He could see a golden light shining in the sky and his heart starting beating like a drum. He braced himself.

When they reached the top of the dune, a blast of sand shot into his eyes, blinding everything from view. Before him lay a large excavation site with metal beams sticking out in awkward directions. Only one anchorage for the steel cables of the city had been built. Gabriel got off his mule and ran down the other side of the dune with his hand over his eyes to ward off the stinging sand. As he scanned the horizon for the Company offices, he felt a brutal blow to his head and everything went black.

Gabriel woke up to a stinging pain and he looked down at the bullet-hole wound. Hanging out of his arm was the black, fat-tailed scorpion from his dream. He shrieked and ripped the animal's stinger from his skin and threw it into the air. Gabriel knew that this particular scorpion was Androctonus crassicauda, the only scorpion in all of Turkistan with a fatal sting. Gabriel began to panic as he felt the neurotoxins entering his bloodstream. He felt heat and saw white flashes. "So this is what death is like," he said to himself. But he could still move and breath. Was it a miracle? Then something told him not to be afraid. One way or another, he found it utterly unfathomable how he'd come in contact with this mystical creature and something about it felt right. He no longer seemed to really care whether or not the poison killed him. In fact, he was almost excited to see what would happen. He looked up into the sky and called out like a savage. The thundering clouds overhead answered him back and he knew they were

telling him to return to the village. His mind became a blur. The horizon started moving and the dunes began to change positions. His briefcase and his wallet where gone. Then he realized the cross Marianne had put around his neck wasn't there. Gabriel didn't care anymore. His head was pounding with such a rhythmic force it began to dance with the pulse of the landscape around him. His stomach growled from hunger, but he didn't care as he had felt himself vomit up whatever was left of the dog leg the officer had given him days before. Then his throat seemed to freeze in a continuous gag reflex. The throbbing grew even more intense and he pushed at his temples, but the pulsing blood running through his brain became a drum and the wind became music. When he finally pulled his hands away everything seemed clearer. It was as if he was in a protective bubble and neither the sand nor the wind could penetrate it.

94

CHAPTER
10

Gabriel realized that if the scorpion didn't kill him, then it would only make him stronger. "That guide and the hotel owner will pay for what they've done," said Gabriel to himself. "I'll mangle the two of them until they've got no choice but to give me everything I want. That's true power," thought Gabriel and suddenly he felt the scorpion venom burn as it surged through his veins.

EVERYTHING WENT BLACK.

CHAPTER II

AFTERNOON
FEATHERS
SILENCE
ON JOURNEY

Gabriel awoke late in the afternoon and a flurry of feathers enveloped him from all sides. He blinked several times before things came into focus. All of a sudden a bird hopped onto his chest and pecked at his eye. Gabriel sat up, grabbed the beast, stuffed it between his legs, and snapped its neck. He blinked several times before realizing it was a rooster. He'd passed out in a chicken coup. Images from his journey with the scorpion venom flashed before his eyes and he laughed. It was a miracle! He was alive. He moved his arms and legs and felt healthier than before. In fact, he'd never felt better in his life. He looked over at his arm and realized it was no longer bleeding and the hole seemed to have almost closed up. His movements were fast and accurate, like the scorpion's sting. He thought that the little black animal he'd met with trembling fingers in the desert had given him something he couldn't get anywhere else, the kind of power that would surge through his veins until his death. Gabriel breathed in the fresh air and grabbed some raw chicken eggs. He began devouring them like an indigenous man and the yolk dribbled down his face.

When Gabriel snuck out of the chicken coup he spotted a well and poured a bucket of water over his head. He realized he was on the outskirts of town and he silently thanked the scorpion for leading him back and sparing his life.

It was late afternoon by the time he reached the hotel. Out back the owner's dogs were harassing a scrawny puppy and Gabriel watched as they chased it around nipping at its heels. The biggest dog grabbed it in its mouth and the whole pack tried to get a piece of the puppy. The sight made Gabriel feel sick.

He ran up to the dogs and they instantly surrounded him, barking ferociously and egging each other on. Gabriel spotted the leader, a big black mutt with a shaggy coat and foam dripping from his tongue. On the ground he saw a pile of glass shards that had fallen from a broken window. He picked up a long piece that was curved like a Shamshir and, with the finesse of a skilled craftsman, he wrapped a palm leaf around it so he could hold it like a knife without cutting himself. The leader growled, bearing his fangs, and Gabriel charged at him with the shard of glass raised in the air. Before the dog even had a chance to open his jaws, Gabriel had driven the shard into his skull.

The other dogs in the pack slowly backed away and, when Gabriel flung the piece of glass, they ran off to the front of the hotel. He peered through a window and, sure enough, there was the hotel owner smiling as he went through Gabriel's luggage trying on his clothes. Kosma was sitting at a table examining the protractor from his drafting kit, which lay open in front of him. They'd assumed he was dead. Gabriel went through a backdoor and once inside he inched through the corridor until he could see the owner sitting in front of him. To his left was a heavy clay jug full of vodka. He grabbed it and went to meet them. By the time the two men were even aware of his presence, Gabriel had already shattered the jug over the owner's skull. Pieces of glass bounced off the walls and slid across the floor. "I've had enough! Where are the goddamn offices?" The owner rolled over on the floor and went for his gun, but Gabriel kicked him in the face and grabbed it, realizing it was the same pistol the officer had given him. Before he could do anything, Gabriel blasted the hotel owner in the right arm and shoved aside the table in front of him. Kosma let out a squeal. As Gabriel walked over to him the guide shut his mouth and dropped the protractor, which stuck in the table vibrating like a dart. "Where's the cross you stole from my neck?" Gabriel yelled pointing the gun in between his beady eyes.

When he didn't answer Gabriel shot him in the leg and hit him in the face with the handle of his pistol. Then Gabriel asked him again. Kosma gurgled up blood and said weakly, "I sold it." "You what?" screamed Gabriel. He lifted the gun and shot a bullet into every limb of Kosma's body until his pistol was empty. Then he kicked over the peasant's chair and he fell to the floor with a crash. "To whom?" Kosma was unable to move and Gabriel just stood over him, watching him squirm on the ground. For a minute he felt another surge of power flow through his body like nothing he'd ever experienced. He walked over to the check-in desk and found another box of ammunition. "You know what? I don't care about the necklace anymore." Gabriel loaded the revolver and shot Kosma in the forehead.

The hotel owner moaned even louder as the sound of the gunshot hung in the dining room. Gabriel grabbed his protractor and walked over to the Georgian, lifting him into a chair by the table with his left arm. He grabbed one of the dirty shirts from his suitcase and tied his arms tightly behind his back before questioning him. "Take me to the office or I'll kill you!" Gabriel said as he brandished the sharp end of the compass in front of the owner's eyes. The man was shaking so much it took him almost a minute before he could reply. "Then kill me because I'll never go back there." Gabriel paced back and forth in the room lost in his thoughts. He almost didn't care about the construction any longer, but he had to get to those offices. He had to learn the truth about what happened to his city and, most of all, he had to know why he'd seen pictures of the construction almost completed. Gabriel grabbed his drafting tools from the peasant's table and he slowly began taking them out of the toolbox like doctor's instruments. "You'd make it a lot easier on yourself if you just took me there." The Georgian winced and let out a scream as Gabriel dug the protractor point into his head. He begged for mercy but Gabriel wouldn't stop as he carved up his face. The scorpion power surged through his veins even faster now. "That's not a civilized way to handle the situation, Duban," said a familiar voice from behind him. Gabriel whirled around to see the officer standing in the middle of the room. "What has he done to deserve this?" asked the officer as he eyed the hotel owner. "I paid him all I had left to find me a guide, but the one he gave me smashed a pipe over my head and left me for dead in the middle of the desert!" For a while the officer was quiet. Then he slowly looked over at the shivering owner and back at Gabriel. "Don't you think there must be something at the offices this man fears more than torture? After all, the human body can withstand only so much pain before it goes numb." Gabriel furrowed his brow. "Why else wouldn't he have already agreed?" "Because he's not taking me there." Gabriel lifted up his pistol and shot the hotel owner in the head and pointed it back at the officer, "You are." The officer was indifferent and unaffected by the threat. Instead, he held out his hand revealing Marianne's necklace with the silver cross. "I believe this is yours." Gabriel was shocked. "How did you…" The officer cut him off. "Your guide was selling it and I remembered you wore it when we met, so I bought it off him." "Thank you," said Gabriel as he lowered his gun. The officer handed him the necklace. "Listen, I'll take you to the valley and from there I can tell you how to get to the offices, but that's as far as I'll go." Gabriel nodded.

CHAPTER
II

CHAPTER 12

SILENCE WINDY ROAD NOTHING BUT SAND

GABRIEL AND THE OFFICER WERE BOTH DRESSED IN THE LOCAL GARB. THE SAND STUNG THEM ON THEIR FACES AND HANDS. GABRIEL HAD A RIFLE SLUNG OVER HIS SHOULDER AND HE STARED OFF INTO SPACE. Gabriel and the officer were both dressed in the local garb. The sand stung them on their faces and hands. Gabriel had a rifle slung over his shoulder and he stared off into space. He noticed his hand was resting on the cross around his neck and he couldn't stop thinking of Marianne. Quickly, he moved it away, but he caught the officer watching him with a sly smile. The men rode for many miles without exchanging any words until finally the officer turned to Gabriel and spoke.

"I'm going to sing you a yoik." "What's that?" asked Gabriel. "It's the song of my people." "Well, be my guest," said Gabriel, half expecting the officer would pull out his accordion. Gabriel was surprised when he lifted a small drum about a foot in diameter from the large rucksack hanging from the side of his mule. The officer then took a small drumstick covered with leather from the bag and began beating the drum and singing in that same ancient language. Strangely, the wind seemed to die down as the officer sang and he felt a calmness surround him.

Gabriel looked at him curiously and he noticed indigenous drawings on his drum that looked almost like petroglyphs. "You're not a Russian?" The officer smiled and laughed

good-heartedly. "I was raised as a Laplander, part of a tribe of people called the Saami." Gabriel looked taken aback. "Where is it?" "The Saami live all over northern Scandinavia and into Russia. I'm from the Kola Peninsula on the Russian side. We lived in small animal-skin houses. The officer nodded his head. "That's how I grew up: herding reindeer, trapping furs, and fishing." Gabriel chuckled at the thought. "How'd you end up an imperial officer?" "I was taken from my home and raised elsewhere," he replied. "When I worked for the viceroy, part of my job was to find out everything I could about you."

The officer was silent for a while before he continued. "In the myths of the Saami, there exists a kind of spirit people who can steal away little children who aren't carrying a special metal amulet for their protection." The officer looked directly at the cross around Gabriel's neck. "Long before Abraham or the Bible, a Saami mother gave birth to a baby and she forgot to give it this amulet. One day she noticed that her baby was behaving abnormally and she became terrified that the spirits had taken him and replaced his spirit with one of theirs. So she asked an old Saami woman for advice and she said, 'Set out a miniature bowl of porridge surrounded by all the spoons in the village, and then you will understand what's happened to your child.' "So the mother did what the old woman told her and she closed the fur hut. When it got dark she peeked inside and watched as the child spoke to itself. It said, 'I've lived longer than the trees and longer than the mountains, but I've never seen anything like it, so many spoons, and so little porridge.' The mother realized then that the spirits had taken her baby and she stormed in with a piece of wood and hit the demon as hard as she could. Afterward, she heard the voices of the spirits wailing. 'Look they've beaten our old grandfather so horribly. We can't stand it any longer.' When the mother opened up the furs it was her own child again and she gave him an amulet not unlike the one you're wearing." "What's that supposed to mean?" said Gabriel. "It means that you're acting like a child whose been inhabited by an evil spirit.

Do not think that surviving the scorpion's sting is an easy task. The power you feel pulsing through your veins requires a great responsibility to control." Gabriel was beginning to get annoyed. "How would you know? You've no idea what I feel." The officer just smiled and rode ahead. "Remember that in ancient legends many scorpions commit suicide by stinging themselves to death. Now you must build up an immunity to your own venom."

It was night when Gabriel and the officer reached the edge of a vast wasteland. The wind blew the sand even harder and both of them had to cover up their faces so only their eyes were visible. The officer turned to Gabriel. "This is where I turn back." "So where are the offices?" "About a kilometer farther if you ride straight ahead." The officer pulled the reins of his mule and rode in a big circle around Gabriel. He gave Gabriel a salute and began riding back toward the town when Gabriel called after the end of his rifle and he lit it on fire like a torch. When he could finally see he called out, "Is anybody here?" There was no answer. He walked behind the front desk and fiddled around until he found several large clockwork levers. One of them had a sign, which read, "chandelier." Gabriel threw the lever up and there was the faint smell of petrol as the giant crystal lamp above his head burst into view with a hundred small candles. He began exploring. The first room on his right was empty so he continued down the corridors that followed. The rest of the building seemed to be in a similar state as the office in Paris, complete with scattered paper and upturned tables.

Finally he made it to a back room where he saw a large table. Beneath it was a model of his colonial city. It was different than the others he'd designed and someone seemed to have made the pillars larger. Also, the fifth pillar he'd mentioned was added to the middle as a giant tube-like tower. Gabriel examined the model with such a deep fascination that he barely noticed when he bumped into something. He was standing in front of a pinhole camera on an old wooden tripod. Its bellows opened in front of his face and he saw it was pointing through a hole in the glass covering the model. His heart sank. "No!" Gabriel said out loud as he realized the newspaper photographs were merely pictures of the model lying before him.

Gabriel picked up the camera on its tripod, closed the legs, and swung it with all of his might against the glass. The lens flew off and cracked on the floor while the whole cover around the model shattered. Gabriel crawled onto the table cutting his hands and knees on the broken shards and kicked the remains of the camera off the tripod as he lifted it over his head again.

"I should've done this long ago!" he cried out as he began smashing the model to pieces in a brutal rage until all energy in his body was drained. Then he slumped down onto the rubble of his smashed city.

So the whole thing had been a scam. Gabriel covered his face with his hands and looked up at the ceiling only to see a dangling body. The man had been dead for quite some time and his face was badly eaten by birds and insects. Gabriel realized he'd finally reached the end of the road. He was ruined, tired, thirsty, and desperate. As he closed his eyes an image of Marianne appeared before him. When he opened them he ripped the necklace from his body and flung it away. He'd lost everything and had no more strength to continue. It was all over. He lay backward and passed out in the middle of his wrecked city.

THE BUILDING WAS JUST AS HE'D REMEMBERED IT FROM THE LITHOGRAPHS IN THE JOURNAL.

CHAPTER 13

MORNING
VISIONS
SECRETS
30ᵀᴴ MARCH

GABRIEL AWOKE AROUND DAWN ONLY TO SEE BRIGHT SUNLIGHT STREAMING THROUGH THE SLANTED WINDOWS ABOVE HIM. A GLOWING SILHOUETTE GRACEFULLY PASSED THROUGH THE DOORWAY AND, BEFORE HE COULD MOVE, SENNA APPEARED ABOVE HIM LIKE A BEAUTIFUL VISION. She caressed his arm and his thoughts became a mixed haze as she kissed him on the forehead. Gabriel was feverish, half awake, half asleep, and unable to move. She opened a box and spread a cream with a strange, but not unpleasant smell on his forehead. The persistent pain he'd had in his temple disappeared and his aching muscles began to relax. Slowly he felt his energy coming back. His breathing began to lighten and he felt as if a weight were being lifted from his chest. Everything still seemed somewhat blurry until Gabriel realized that she was on top of him and they were making love, but he was still unable to move and his body felt weightless.

Gabriel recognized the body hanging overhead – it was Girard surrounded by a cloud of black butterflies. He felt a slight chill of terror, but he couldn't get away. It didn't seem to matter much any longer

111

and he realized he was enjoying himself. He tried to speak, but Senna put her finger to his lips. There would be plenty of time for him to understand everything. She covered herself up while speaking in a soothing whisper. "For reasons I can't discuss, the construction's been moved to a secret location. I'll take you there. These are the viceroy's orders." "Where is he? I must speak with him." "Be patient," said Senna. "Soon you'll understand everything."

She took him by the hand and led him to an exit. Gabriel was blinded by a bright light as the doors opened wide. On each side, a grand expanse of canyon walls rose up and a chariot pulled by two black horses halted in front of them. Gabriel climbed inside and watched as they rumbled along the canyon floor next to a long stream. Eventually the canyon dove back into the sand and they followed the water. As it ran along the rolling dunes it slowly turned into a river. The sun rose and Gabriel watched as the rays peaked over the horizon. After about a half an hour, they reached the coastline of a black lake covered in mist. Gabriel couldn't see across so he had no idea how big the body of water actually was. Standing on the bank was an old boatman holding a rickety oar and Senna beckoned for him to follow her into the boat.

When they reached the center of the lake, the weather began to worsen and Gabriel noticed the boatman was having a hard time rowing. Gabriel scooted him aside and grabbed one of the oars.

As they drifted through the mist, the towering structure of Gabriel's city emerged with all the splendor of a floating, weightless town. It hung over a ruined village much like Kokand and Gabriel let out a long, deep sigh. There it was. Not only was it beautiful, it was real and complete. He was in such awe he seemed to forget about everything. Endless lines of caravans were moving toward the settlement like a great pilgrimage.

A GRAND BALL WAS GOING TAKING PLACE AND AN ORCHESTRA WAS PLAYING.

Eventually they arrived at an anchorage holding some of the town's giant suspended cables. Large gates and dense, spiked wire fences surrounded the entire construction and even the train station seemed to be under impenetrable security. Gabriel followed Senna's lead as they maneuvered through the customs. The guards looked similar to the ones from the Paris office and they tipped their hats to Gabriel as he passed.

When they'd moved through the anchorage, a strange locomotive waited on a set of tracks that led up a hanging bridge into town. The security seemed very high, like in a big prison camp. Gabriel was awakening from the cold wind and started to remember why he was here. "The guards aren't very welcoming, are they?" he said to Senna. "We must do what's necessary to protect the city from intruders and enemies." Gabriel spotted a palace in the center of the structure. "Are we going there?" "That's the viceroy's headquarters, but you can't just go there directly, nobody can. First you must meet with other officials in charge, then we'll pass through a third customs and finally you must pass a test in order to gain entrance." "A test!" said Gabriel.

THEY DRIFTED THROUGH THE MIST. THE TOWERING STRUCTURE EMERGED WITH ALL SPLENDOR OF A NEOCLASSICAL TOWN.

"I didn't make the rules," Senna replied as she gently turned Gabriel's head toward the city.

Gabriel gasped in wonder as they rode through. He watched festivities that were being conducted for some of the first visitors. The place was familiar and strange at the same time. He saw little rickshaw cars pulled by men and ostriches. There were children flying kites and girls flying on swings attached to giant steel cables far above the city. It was so strange and amazing for him to walk through his own drawings. A grand ball was going on and an orchestra was playing. Dancing couples drank from tall glasses. Gabriel even thought he recognized several Parisian ladies from his neighborhood whispering in the ears of some statesman.

There were horses pulling cable cars and the employees were chained to the structure, making navigation complicated. The horses were also secured with cables, which were attached to rails allowing them to slide along distinguished paths, and parents held their kids on leashes. The wind began to pick up and hats and scarves flew into the air. "What about those cables, are you sure we're safe?" Senna smiled coolly. "They're just precautions in case a storm breaks out." The weather was changing every minute; colors were shifting from blue to purple. Senna's dress was alternating between orange and scarlet red. Gabriel saw some uncompleted parts of the city that looked like huge suspended scaffolding. The wind picked up the rose from Senna's hair and sent it into the sky.

They reached a second checkpoint that blocked the unfinished part of the city that also closed off the entrance to the palace. The security was even higher. The guard's ankles were chained to the structure and the cables that hung from the city looked like a giant spider web. The wind was turning piercingly cold and made Gabriel shiver. The guards stopped him and tried to bind him in cuffs, but he resisted and struggled free. Senna grabbed him. "Look, this is for your own security. Just let them put them on and the guards will take you to see the viceroy." Gabriel felt trapped. He felt like the whole city was a giant cage. "No, I'll go by myself," he said. He ran and jumped over a railing into the underbelly of the structure. Just a small grid-like boardwalk was in between him and certain death and he saw a small cloud floating beneath him. One of the huge guards swung down on his cable lunging at him and grabbed his leg with a vice-like grip. Gabriel landed a well-aimed kick in his head and he rolled off the side of the boardwalk. The guard's cable whipped tight and he lost control as he hurtled into some metal beams, smashing his head on his way down. Gabriel winced as a cloud of blood floated off in the wind, but he felt strong, awake, and fearless.

He regained his balance and ran down the boardwalk. Everything was exactly as he remembered it from his drawings and there was no way any of the guards could outsmart him. He was concentrating with his eyes half closed, hardly needing to look at his path. He made flying leaps between the cables and always landed where he aimed. Then he spotted one of the main launch pads for guards. One of the cables led over the wall and into the palace grounds. Nearby were hanging harnesses and he snapped one onto one of the small engines that moved along the cables, putting his legs through it like a rock climber. Each engine was equipped with a small lever for acceleration and a hand brake for controlling the speed. Behind him were two more guards. With a running start he flew off the platform and began zipping down the structure with mathematical precision. Gabriel narrowly missed being shredded by the barbed fence in front of the palace. He looked behind him to see the two guards were too clumsy and heavy. They smashed into the palace wall and fell on the metal spikes and wires. He quickly hit the brake as he came to a gentle halt on the palace grounds.

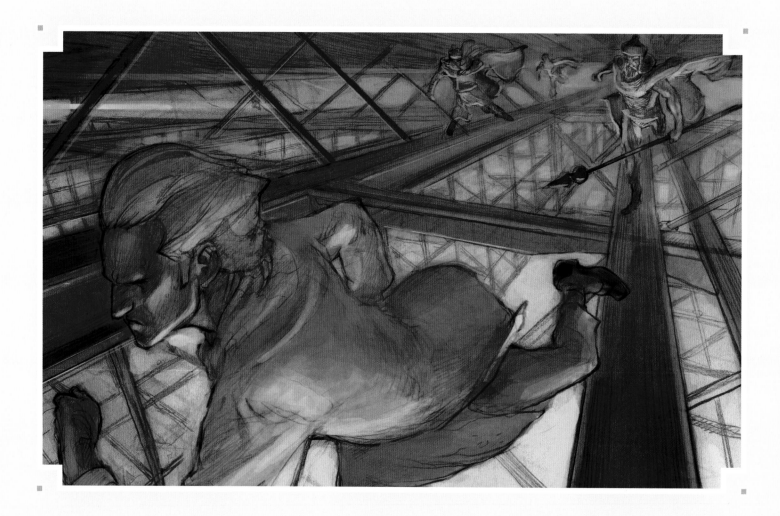

He snuck over to a place where he saw an open manhole and he crawled under the city. There were ramps and boardwalks on the underside of the palace and he clipped his harness onto one of the railings so he wouldn't fall. He walked along until he found a giant tube that led upward and he knew he was right below the palace. Guards started climbing up a ladder toward him. Gabriel spotted a fire -ax on the wall and pulled it off. As one guard reached up to grab his leg, Gabriel spun around and chopped off some of his fingers. The guard fell backwards knocking down a few more men.

Gabriel finally came out of the tube only to realize he'd been climbing the fifth central pillar. Abruptly he experienced vertigo and proportions began to change and mutate. He looked down and saw the silhouettes of guards trapped in the cables like flies in a spider web. A terrible storm was on the horizon and he snapped his harness to the side of the tube. He held on as he watched the wind blow pieces of the city into the sky. The city began swinging like a ship on stormy seas. A sandstorm picked up and scarves, umbrellas, and people started flying off in all directions and were sucked into the heavens.

GIRLS SWINGING ON WOODEN SEATS ATTACHED TO GIANT STEEL CABLES FAR ABOVE THE CITY.

The guards who were chained to the structure floated in the air like kites next to their horses and dogs. Gabriel fought with the storm as he tried to climb back down the pillar, but the building swayed so violently he couldn't move. Eventually all of the metal sheets fixed on the pillar were sucked away and he clung onto the end of a giant metal ladder. Cables on one of the pillars started to snap and the building tilted and half crashed to the ground. Gabriel hung onto his ladder as it bent over and deposited him at the front door of the palace. The floor was tilted at a 15-degree angle. Gabriel staggered over to the palace gate and pushed it open. He walked through a long, empty hallway until he reached a door very similar to the one at the Company office in Turkistan. He pushed it open and entered. The place was strangely quiet, like an abandoned labyrinth. He walked around to the back and discovered the same room he'd passed out in with the model. Was it a déjà vu?

At the other end of the hall was a tall red curtain that, as he approached it, was pulled aside to reveal a stage. Behind it Gabriel witnessed a picturesque group waiting for him.

The viceroy was dressed in all black, except for a large white collar, and next to him stood several strange men all wearing suits from some ancient, undefined time period. Senna sat almost naked next to a giant cat dressed in a suit, and no armed guards were present.

Gabriel walked in swinging the fire ax by his side. "I'm very pleased to meet you again, your majesty! I went through quite a bit of trouble to get here," he said smiling, "but I'm glad we'll have the opportunity to complete our business transaction." One character from the entourage whispered to another one and it traveled down the line. "Saying you put me through hell would be mild at most, you crook, with your fancy suits and shiny gold buttons. Where are the henchmen? Pity, your entourage doesn't look like they'll make for much of a lively audience when I crucify you on your own throne. Now, I'll get all the information I need to prove my innocence. I'll also drag your head back to Paris after your lovely assistant kindly takes me to the loot. Don't think I'm intimidated by your superhuman reputation, because I feel pretty good myself." Senna stood up and spoke. "You have no right to accuse us of a false deal. Your city's already built, your reputation in Paris is cleared, your family will be provided for, and the payment's yours. Now it's time for you to hold up your end of the bargain." "What's that? You got my design so now I want what's mine." "That wasn't our deal, Gabriel." "In the contract it clearly states in Section 1.1: GABRIEL DUBAN AGREES TO DEVOTE THE TIME NECESSARY IN ORDER TO PERFORM THE SERVICES AND DELIVER THE REQUIRED DELIVERABLES IN ACCORDANCE TO THIS AGREEMENT AND TO MEET THE NEEDS OF THE COMPANY. THE AGREEMENT SHALL COMMENCE ON THE EFFECTIVE DATE SET FORTH BY THE COMPANY AND SHALL REMAIN IN EFFECT UNTIL THE FINAL SERVICES PROVIDED BY THE CONTRACTOR ARE DEFINED AND VALIDATED BY THE COMPANY. ONLY LE COMPAGNIE UNIVERSELLE HAS THE RIGHT TO TERMINATE THE AGREEMENT."

"That's not a contract, that's imprisonment. What could the company possibly need now? You've taken everything from me." "It's not defined. You see, Gabriel, once you signed this contract, you were in the hands of the viceroy, and it's up to him to determine what the company needs." "But, that could mean anything! I didn't know I made a deal with the devil."

A gentle glow blossomed in the Orlof's eyes and a smile broke out across his face. He opened his mouth and began to speak for the first time since Gabriel met him. It was impossible to tell whether he was singing, talking, or crying. Either way, a symphony erupted out of nowhere and it accompanied his voice. Gabriel understood every word as if they were being engraved onto his brain.

YOU GOT MY DESIGN. SO NOW I GET THE PAYMENT.

HUNDREDS OF MINIATURE STRUCTURES WERE LINED UP IN AN ENDLESS WAREHOUSE.

CHAPTER
13

"Dear Gabriel, our deal was but a game;
Now the end has started flipped upside down,
Your divine blueprint brought us worldly fame,
But the venture is still a broken crown;
If painless journeys were your only aim,
Then your soul travels not above the ground.
And about these powers, super human;
My goblet sings with a time bending sound;
I will turn back the clock within a frame,
Before the dream in desert sand was drowned;
Now you ought to make the choice once again,
Of how your city's greatness will be found."

Gabriel was silent as he focused on the poem and his fist tightened around the ax handle. His eyes were fixed on the tip of the viceroy's finger as it circled the rim of a crystal goblet. A high-pitched sound resonated throughout the room and the ringing hung in the air as the lights faded to black.

Suddenly Gabriel was standing on the Ministry stairs in front of Girard's office. It was February 10, 1875. Gabriel looked at his pocket watch. It was twelve-thirty, 15 minutes before Girard had asked him to withdraw his project from the competition. He heard Jules's voice from behind Girard's door. "Sir, don't forget that today you agreed to meet with Duban." Girard grunted, "Aw, yes, your childhood friend? Has he been warned he's only got five minutes?" "Yes, sir." "Jules, let us be clear on the following. I'll take the time to listen to him, but I hope you know he doesn't stand a chance of being promoted. He should withdraw his inadequate project from the competition! It's likely he won't last much longer at the Ministry anyways. Duban's profile doesn't exactly suit our strategy." Jules walked up the stairs and into Gabriel's office. Gabriel started drafting, and his eyes followed the same line of ink as it flowed onto the same pristine sheet of white drafting paper. He watched his hands moving with extreme efficiency as he quickly marked the blueprint again. Everything was exactly as he remembered it. "Duban!" said Jules. This time Gabriel was ready and he lifted his pen to avoid smudging the drawing. "Sorry, Gabriel. Girard's waiting." Gabriel didn't reply and when he turned around he was standing in front of Orlof. He dropped his ax and stared at the ceiling. Senna approached him and put her arms around him softly stroking his back. He felt a hot breath against his ear as she began to whisper,

"You see, the promotion was never yours to begin with and the only way you would have gotten the city built is through us. You've become the architect of your own pre-manufactured hell." Confused, Gabriel replied, "Yeah, but I can't stay here. My wife and my son are waiting for me." "But wouldn't you rather they be proud of you for finishing the project, or would you rather go back to Paris as a failure?" Gabriel said nothing and Senna took him by the hand. "Now the viceroy will lead you to greatness." Orlof pointed to another red curtain. The fabric was pulled aside to reveal a grand workshop gallery. It was a majestic room full of miniature structures and devices that were lined up in an endless warehouse. Gabriel walked among them and he saw the Tower of Babel, a beautiful miniature of a golden El Dorado, and thousands more strange cities and towers. The warehouse was home to every utopian city in human history.

Gabriel marveled as he walked through the room, and then a waltz began to play. Another red curtain parted and a grand orchestra was revealed. Senna moved behind him, grabbed him, and enveloped him in the swirl of a dance.

CHAPTER
13

EPILOGUE
END

PARIS
MARIANNE'S
HOME
A LETTER

MARIANNE WAS AMID
NEWSPAPER CLIPPINGS THAT RECOUNTED THE DETAILS OF HER HUSBAND'S
DISAPPEARANCE IN THE DESERTS OF ASIA MINOR WHEN SHE HEARD A LOUD
KNOCK AT THE DOOR. She opened it to see the officer dressed as a postman. He was
holding a letter and a box, which he gave to Marianne without a word. She closed the
door and opened the letter. Inside she found a check signed by her beloved husband,
along with careful instructions on how she was to distribute the money to the victims
of the Company's bankruptcy. There was nothing more written and she quickly tore
open the package hoping to find some clue as to her husband's
whereabouts. In the midst of some old paper packing was a strange
glass orb. Marianne picked it up and held it to her forehead. Inside was
a deeply intricate model city made of steel, glass, and concrete.
The thing looked otherworldly, as if it were a cyclopean mass of
plant-like buildings and endless sprawling pipes and interchanging
in every direction imaginable.

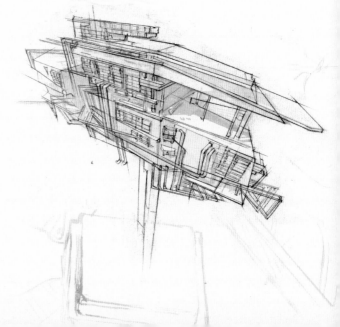

TO CONTACT THE AUTHOR
PLEASE E-MAIL TO
VIKTOR@THEBUILDINGSTUDIOS.COM

OR YOU CAN VISIT
WWW.VULKANBROS.COM

FOR VOLUME PURCHASES
& RESALE INQUIRIES
PLEASE E-MAIL TO
INFO@DESIGNSTUDIOPRESS.COM

OR YOU CAN WRITE TO
DESIGN STUDIO PRESS
8577 HIGUERA STREET
CULVER CITY, CA 90232
TEL. 310.836.3116
FAX. 310.836.1136

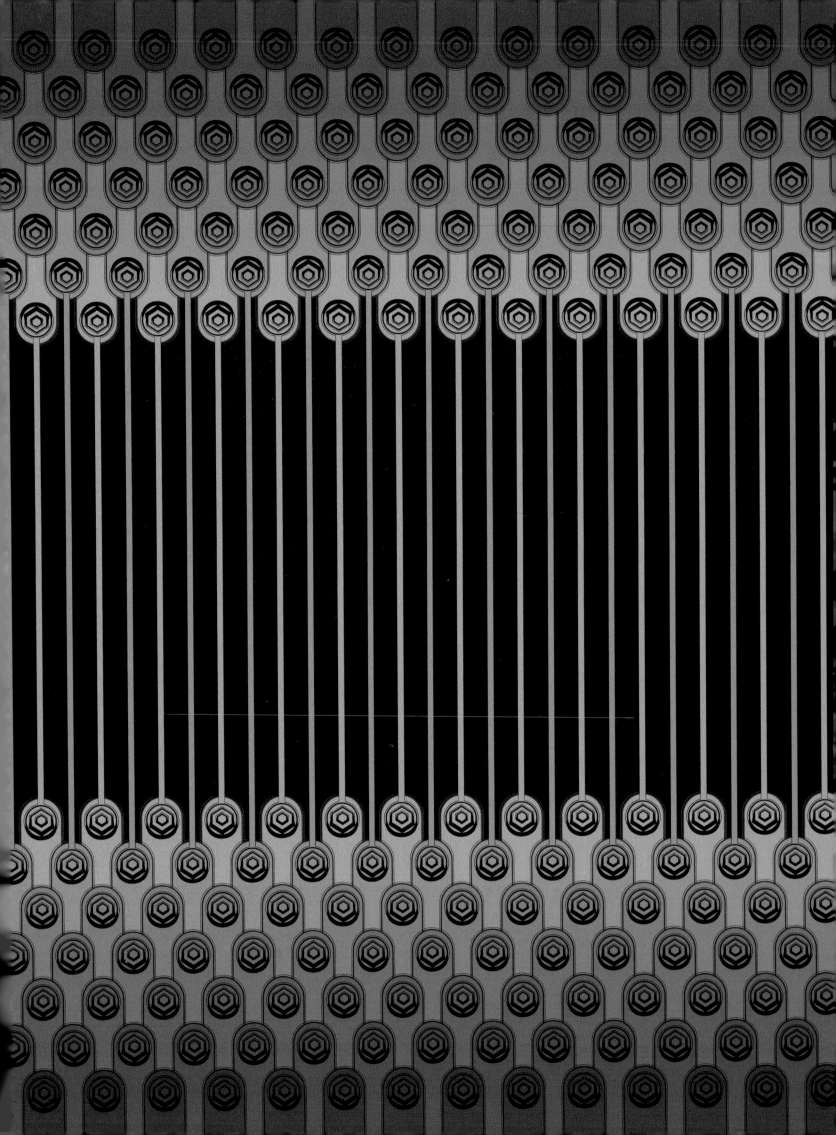